Electronics
Third level

Hutchinson TECtexts

Learning by Objectives
A Teachers' Guide
A. D. Carroll, J. E. Duggan and R. Etchells

Engineering Drawing and Communication
First Level
P. Collier and R. Wilson

Physical Science
First Level
A. D. Carroll, J. E. Duggan and R. Etchells

Workshop Processes and Materials
First Level
P. Collier and B. Parkinson

Electronics
Second Level
G. Billups and M. T. Sampson

Engineering Drawing
Second Level
P. Collier and R. Wilson

Engineering Science
Second Level
D. Tipler, A. D. Carroll and R. Etchells

Mathematics
Second Level
G. W. Allan and A. Hill

Site Surveying and Levelling
Second Level
J. Pettet

Electronics
Third Level
G. Billups and M. T. Sampson

Communication Skills
P. Panton

General Studies for Technicians
P. Denham, H. Bamforth and J. Derbyshire

Hutchinson
TECtexts

Electronics

Third Level

G. Billups & M. T. Sampson

Hutchinson
London Melbourne Sydney Auckland Johannesburg

Hutchinson & Co. (Publishers) Ltd

An imprint of the Hutchinson Publishing Group

17-21 Conway Street, London W1P 6JD

Hutchinson Group (Australia) Pty Ltd
30-32 Cremorne Street, Richmond South, Victoria 3121
PO Box 151, Broadway, New South Wales 2007

Hutchinson Group (NZ) Ltd
32-34 View Road, PO Box 40-086, Glenfield, Auckland 10

Hutchinson Group (SA) (Pty) Ltd
PO Box 337, Bergvlei 2012, South Africa

First published 1979
Reprinted 1983

Printed in Great Britain by The Anchor Press Ltd
and bound by Wm Brendon & Son Ltd
both of Tiptree, Essex

British Library Cataloguing in Publication Data
Sampson, M. T.
Electronics, Third Level – (Hutchinson TECtexts)
1. Electronic apparatus and appliances
I. Title
II. Billups, G.
621.381 TK7870

ISBN 0 09 140341 3

Contents

Introduction 7

Field effect transistors 9

Amplifiers 37

Noise 68

Simple resistive capacitive networks 97

Oscillators 113

Integrated circuits 153

Stabilized power supplies 164

Index 173

Introduction

In each of the books in this series the authors have written text material to specified objectives. Test questions are provided to enable the reader to evaluate the objectives. The solutions or answers are given to all questions.

Topic area Field effect transistors

After reading the following material, the reader shall:

1 Describe the action of a field effect transistor (FET).
1.1 Describe the basic construction of FETs (junction gate and insulated gate).
1.2 Describe the operation of FETs.
1.3 Explain the difference between depletion and enhancement modes.
1.4 Determine the output and transfer characteristics from given data.
1.5 Compare the properties of an FET with valves and bipolar transistors.
1.6 State the precautions used when using FETs.

The field effect transistor (FET) possesses very similar properties to those of the bipolar transistor; namely high efficiency, ease of construction, instant operation, low noise generation, and usually low heat dissipation. It is also robust and cheap. The FET may be utilized in most circuit applications which use bipolar transistors. The FET does have one major advantage over the bipolar transistor in that it has a high input impedance and is therefore more adaptable than its bipolar counterpart. The FET finds extensive use in circuitry where the signal-to-noise ratio is of prime importance, such as r.f. and audio amplifiers. A disadvantage with FETs is that they are quite vulnerable to various kinds of electrical damage. The problem is now being overcome by manufacturers who are integrating diodes into some FETs as a safeguard.

FETs are in fact the semiconductor equivalent of the triode thermionic valve. Their operation is dependent upon the production of a current in a semiconductor material (p- or n-type) by an electrostatic field, i.e. the field effect principle. In some circuits FETs may be substituted directly for low power triode valves.

FETs were theoretically evolved in 1928 but have only recently been commercially manufactured with any success as a result of the advancement of integrated circuit technology. FETs have many applications in electronics. They are used as the active devices in amplifier systems, logic circuits, oscillators, d.c. voltmeters and analogue circuits. They are also used both as the active and passive devices (i.e. transistors and resistors) in integrated circuits.

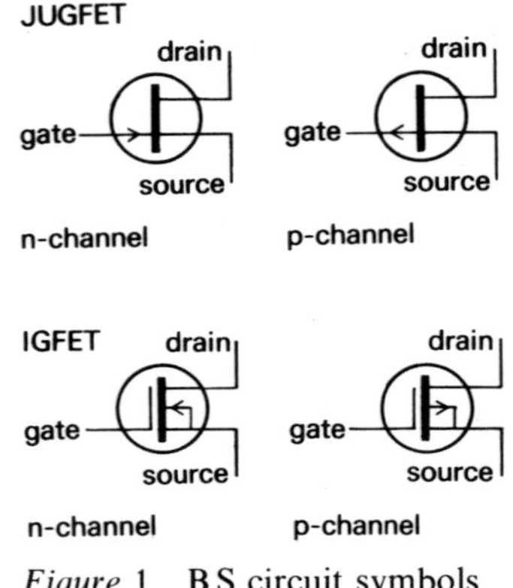

Figure 1 BS circuit symbols for FETs

FETs are unipolar devices. Under the influence of an electric field only majority carriers are used for conveying current through them. There are two main types of field effect transistor:

(i) *the junction gate FET*, sometimes referred to as the JUGFET
(ii) *the insulated gate FET*, sometimes referred to as the IGFET or MOSFET (metal oxide semiconductor FET).

Both of these types are available in either p- or n-channel form, just like p-n-p and n-p-n bipolar transistors. They may be used for similar applications, but the MOSFET is generally used where high input impedances are required to reduce loading effects, for example, in audio amplifiers and electronic instruments.

Figure 1 illustrates the BS circuit symbols for p- and n-channel JUGFETs and IGFETs. Like the bipolar transistor, the field effect transistor (unipolar transistor) is a three terminal device. The electrodes are designated the source, the gate and the drain:

(i) the *source* is the source of current carriers
(ii) the *gate* controls the amount of current flowing through the device
(iii) the *drain* is the electrode from which the majority carriers are 'drained' from the device.

Junction gate FET

Both p- and n-channel JUGFETs are available. A p-channel JUGFET is doped with trivalent (acceptor) impurity which gives rise to a channel current consisting of holes. (Remember a hole is the deficiency of an electron.) An n-channel JUGFET is doped with a pentavalent (donor) impurity which gives rise to a channel current consisting of electrons. Since electrons have a greater mobility than the 'apparent' movement of holes, n-channel JUGFETs are more efficient than p-channel types and thus are more popular, particularly for high frequency applications. Since the JUGFET is available in complementary form it may be used with either a positive or negative earth supply.

Figure 2(*a*) shows a cross-section of a silicon planar diffused n-channel JUGFET; the source and drain are connected by an n-type semiconductor channel. With no external voltages applied, the junctions formed between the n-channel and the p-type material are in fact p-n junctions so that depletion layers are formed. The depletion layers extend into the n-channel as shown in Figure 2(*b*).

Figure 3 shows the n-channel JUGFET with two bias voltages applied to it: (i) a positive voltage applied to the drain with respect to the source, and (ii) a negative voltage applied to the gate with respect to the source.

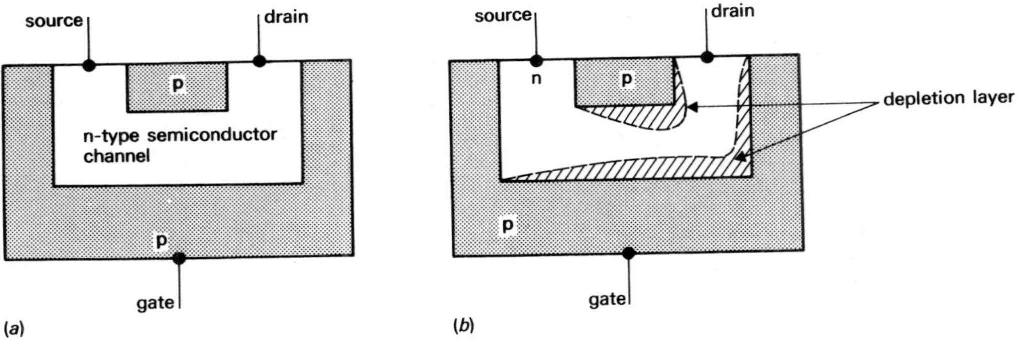

Figure 2 (a) Planer diffused n-channel F E T
(b) n-channel F E T showing depletion layers

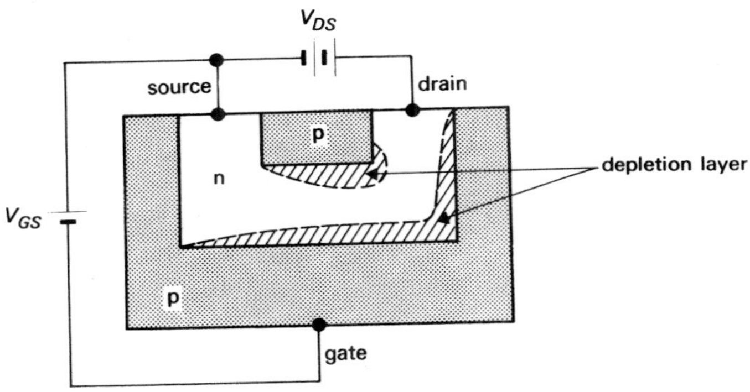

Figure 3 n-channel F E T with bias voltages applied

Consider now the two bias voltages separately. With zero gate–source voltage and a small drain–source voltage V_{DS}, applied as shown in Figure 4(*a*), electrons are attracted from the source to the drain. This flow of electrons is the drain–source current I_{DS}. As the drain–source voltage is increased, the drain–source current also increases; the n-channel behaves as a resistor. During this increase in drain–source voltage, the depletion layers widen, since the p-n junction between the gate and the channel is a reverse biased one. Further increase in the drain–source voltage causes the depletion layers to widen to such an extent that it closes completely, as shown in Figure 4(*b*). The drain–source current is then restricted. The point where the depletion layer closes is called the *pinch-off point* and the drain–source voltage is called the pinch-off voltage V_p.

If the drain-source voltage is now increased beyond the pinch-off voltage, there is no change in the drain–source current, i.e. *saturation* has occurred. This value of the current is known as the drain–source saturation current I_{DSS}. If the drain–source voltage is increased to a sufficiently high value, the gate–channel junction breaks down and permanent damage to the FET may result.

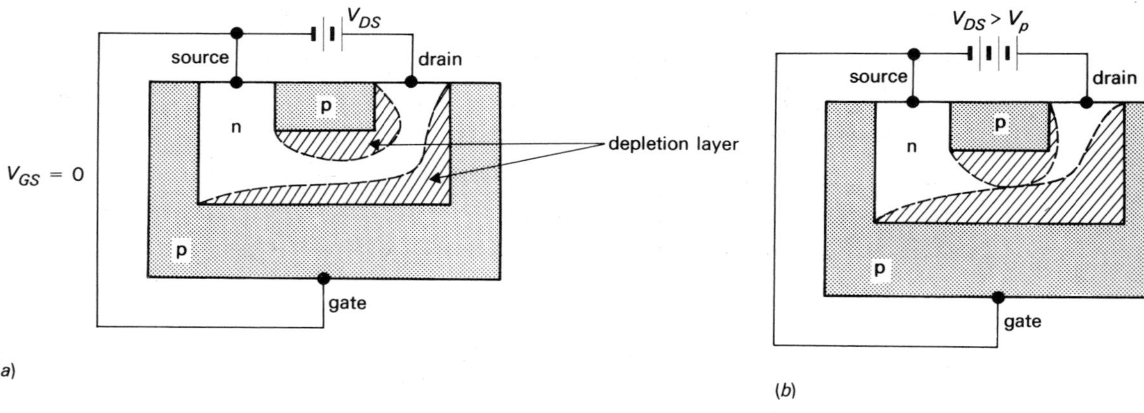

Figure 4 (a) n-channel F E T with $V_{GS}=0$
(b) n-channel F E T at pinch-off

With zero drain–source voltage and a negative voltage applied to th gate as shown in Figure 5(*a*), the reverse biased junction depletic layers once again increase. As the gate voltage is increased, th depletion layers widen further until pinch-off occurs, as shown i Figure 5(*b*). This time pinch-off occurs earlier and at a low saturation current.

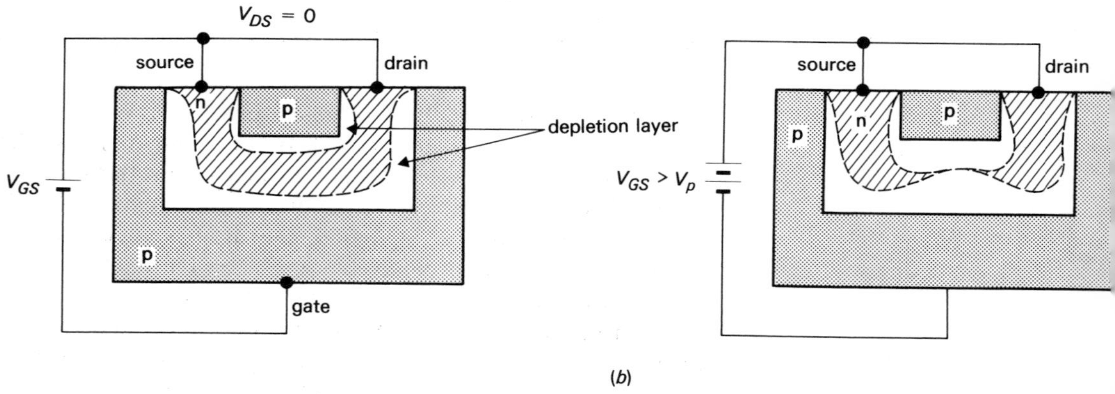

Figure 5 (a) n-channel F E T with $V_{DS}=0$
(b) n-channel F E T at pinch-off

The effect of the two biasing voltages acting together can be seen fron the typical output characteristics of Figure 6. The characteristics ar divided into three distinct regions – the *triode region*, the *pinch-o region* and the *breakdown region*. In the triode region, both the gat source voltage V_{GS} and the drain–source voltage V_{DS} control th channel current I_D. The FET behaves as a linear resistor in this region and is utilized for this purpose in integrated circuits. In the pinch-o

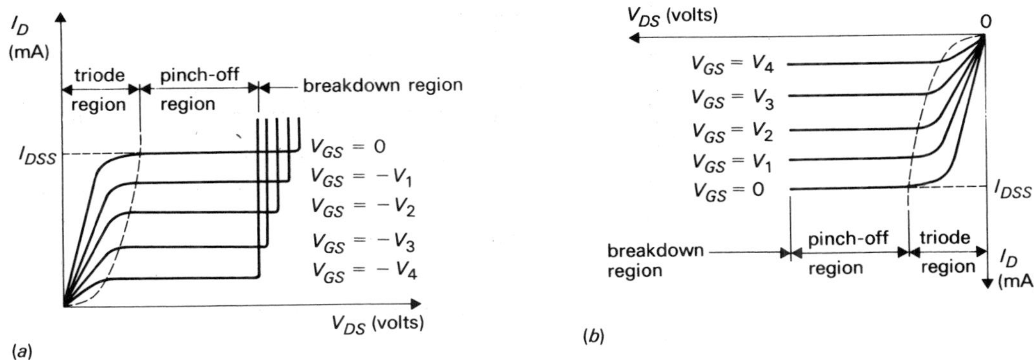

Figure 6 (a) Typical output characteristic of an n-channel JUGFET
(b) Typical output characteristic of a p-channel JUGFET

region the gate–source voltage controls the channel current; the drain–source voltage has little effect. The broken line shows the locus of all the drain–source pinch-off voltages for various gate bias potentials. As the gate voltage becomes more negative, pinch-off occurs at progressively lower values of drain current and drain–source voltage. The control of the drain current by a negative gate potential makes the FET useful as a switch.

It is essential that the gate voltage is never positive; if it were, all the channel current would flow to the gate and not to the drain: the result would be damage to the FET.

The p-channel JUGFET operates in a similar manner to the n-channel JUGFET with two exceptions:

(i) channel current is due to the movement of holes; and
(ii) the polarity of the biasing voltage needs to be reversed. Typical output characteristics of a p-channel JUGFET are shown in Figure 6(*b*).

Insulated gate FET (IGFET)

The IGFET (or MOSFET) differs from the JUGFET in that it has a metal gate electrode which is electrically insulated from the channel by a thin layer of insulating material, usually silicon dioxide. This is how the name MOSFET was derived – metal oxide semiconductor FET. Two types of MOSFET are available:

(*a*) *n-channel types.* An increase in the reverse bias gate voltage reduces the drain–source current, i.e. a voltage is required to turn the device off. These types are usually *depletion mode* devices.
(*b*) *p-channel types.* There is *no* drain–source current when the gate voltage is zero, and the gate voltage needs to be negative for drain–source current to flow, i.e. a voltage is required to turn the device on. These types are usually *enhancement mode* devices.

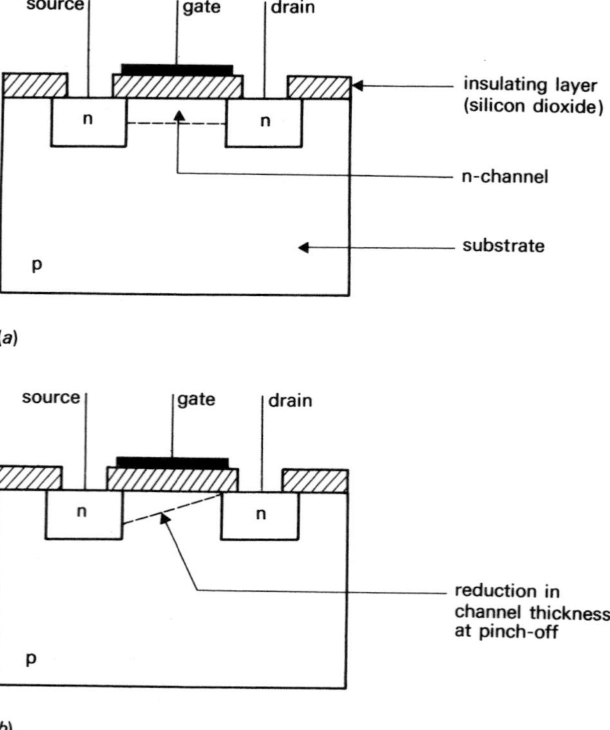

Figure 7 (a) Planar diffused n-channel depletion mode MOSFET
(b) n-channel depletion mode MOSFET

It is possible to manufacture the p-channel depletion and the n-channel enhancement types of MOSFET but they are not as common as the n-channel depletion and the p-channel enhancement types.

Figure 7(*a*) shows a cross-section of a silicon, planar, diffused, n-channel, depletion mode MOSFET. This is formed from a p-type substrate into which are diffused two n-type regions which form the source and the drain. The insulating layer (silicon dioxide) covers the surface of the p-type substrate. A metal gate (gold or aluminium) is then deposited on the insulating layer between the n-regions to form the gate electrode. When the gate voltage is zero, and the drain-source voltage is increased, the drain current increases linearly until pinch-off is reached. At pinch-off, the n-channel becomes closed at the drain end as shown in Figure 7(*b*). If the gate voltage is now increased negatively with respect to the source, the n-channel again closes, but this time at lower values of drain saturation current, i.e. the channel has been depleted of free electrons. The MOSFET is now operating in the depletion mode. Figure 8 shows the typical output characteristics of an n-channel MOSFET operating in the depletion mode. It can be

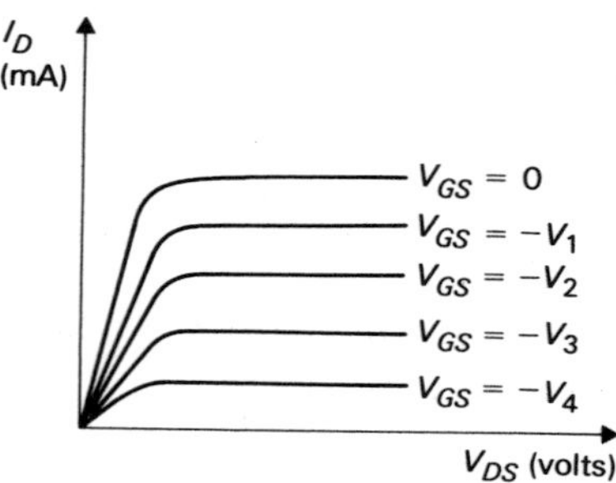

Figure 8 Output characteristic of an n-channel depletion mode MOSFET

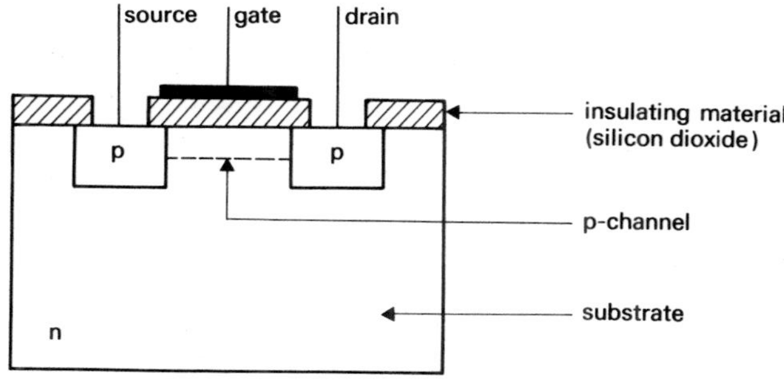

Figure 9 Planar diffused p-channel enhancement mode MOSFET

seen from the characteristics that the depletion mode MOSFET is a normally *on* device – a reverse gate voltage being required to turn it *off*.

Figure 9 shows a cross-section of a silicon, planar, diffused, p-channel, enhancement mode MOSFET. This is formed from an n-type substrate into which are diffused two p-type regions which form the source and the drain. The insulating layer (silicon dioxide) covers the surface of the n-type substrate. A metal gate (gold or aluminium) is then deposited on the insulating layer between the p-type regions to form the gate electrode. In the enhancement mode, the p-channel MOSFET operates with a negative voltage applied to the drain with respect to the source, and a negative voltage applied to the gate with respect to the source. When the gate–source voltage is zero, no drain current flows even when the drain–source voltage is increased, since one of the p-n junctions is reverse biased. If now the negative gate voltage is increased, a p-type channel is formed and hole conduction takes place. This hole conduction increases as the gate–source voltage increases. The MOSFET is now operating in the enhancement mode. Figure 10 illustrates the output characteristics of a p-channel MOSFET. It can be seen from the characteristics that the enhancement mode MOSFET is a normally *off* device – a reverse gate voltage being required to turn it *on*.

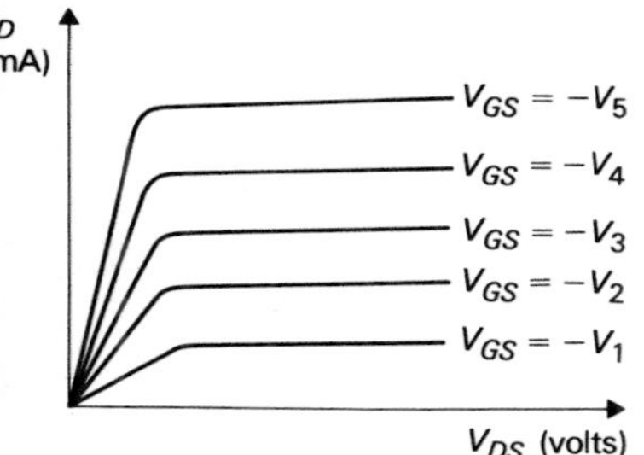

Figure 10 Output characteristic of a p-channel enhancement mode MOSFET

FET characteristics

Using the circuit of Figure 11, the output and transfer characteristics of an n-channel FET can be determined. Initially, the drain–source voltage V_{DS}, and the gate–source voltage V_{GS}, are set to zero by adjusting potentiometers V_{R2} and V_{R1} respectively. The potentiometer V_{R2} is adjusted in order to increase the drain–source voltage V_{DS} by suitable increments. At each incremental increase, values of the drain current I_D are measured. It is unwise to increase V_{DS} beyond 25 V or damage to the FET may occur. The procedure is repeated for V_{GS}

values of $-0{\cdot}5$V, $-1{\cdot}0$ V, $-1{\cdot}5$ V, $-2{\cdot}0$ V, $-2{\cdot}5$ V and $-3{\cdot}0$ V. The tabulated results obtained in the laboratory for a 2N3819 n-channel FET (Radiospares) can be seen in Table 1.

drain–source voltage V_{DS} (volts)	drain current I_D (mA)						
	$V_{GS}=0$V	$V_{GS}=-0{\cdot}5$V	$V_{GS}=-1{\cdot}0$V	$V_{GS}=-1{\cdot}5$V	$V_{GS}=-2{\cdot}0$V	$V_{GS}=-2{\cdot}5$V	$V_{GS}=-3{\cdot}0$V
1	3·6	3·20	2·60	2·05	1·45	0·50	0·40
2	6·00	5·00	4·05	3·00	2·00	1·00	0·42
3	7·00	6·00	4·70	3·35	2·20	1·20	0·45
4	7·84	6·30	4·90	3·45	2·30	1·30	0·50
5	8·00	6·40	5·00	3·60	2·35	1·40	0·58
10	8·15	6·50	5·10	3·75	2·50	1·45	0·65
15	8·20	6·60	5·20	3·78	2·55	1·50	0·70
20	8·20	6·70	5·25	3·79	2·60	1·58	0·75
25	8·20	6·80	5·30	3·80	2·65	1·60	0·77

Table 1 Results obtained in the laboratory from the circuit of Figure 11

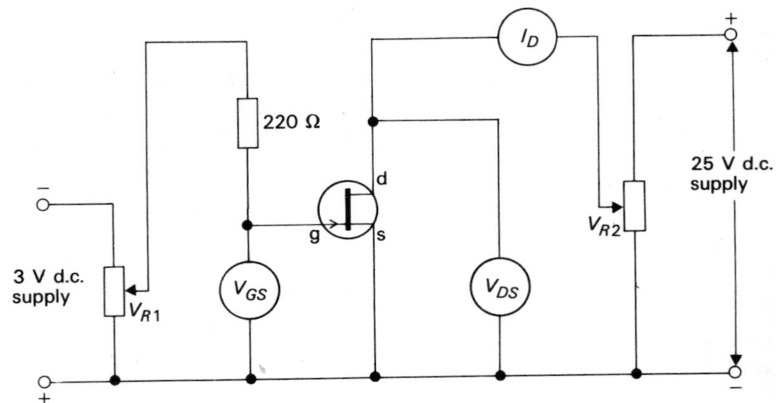

Figure 11 Circuit for determining the output and transfer characteristics of n-channel JUGFET (2N3819 Radiospares)

Output characteristics

Using the results of Table 1, the output characteristics of the FET can be plotted. The output characteristics are graphs of the drain–source voltage V_{DS}, against drain current I_D, for constant values of gate–source voltage V_{GS}. The output characteristics for the 2N3819 n-channel FET can be seen in Figure 12. Indicated on the characteristics are

(i) the pinch-off region
(ii) the drain saturation current at pinch-off I_{DSS}
(iii) the pinch-off voltage V_P, at $V_{GS}=0$ V
(iv) the locus of all the pinch-off voltages.

The incremental slope at any point on the output characteristics is termed the *incremental channel resistance* r_{DS}. Sometimes its reciprocal g_{OS}, the *output conductance*, is quoted, i.e.

$$r_{DS}=\frac{\text{small change in drain source voltage}}{\text{small change in drain current}}\text{ for constant } V_{GS}$$

and

$$g_{OS}=\frac{\text{small change in drain current}}{\text{small change in drain–source voltage}}\text{ for constant } V_{GS}$$

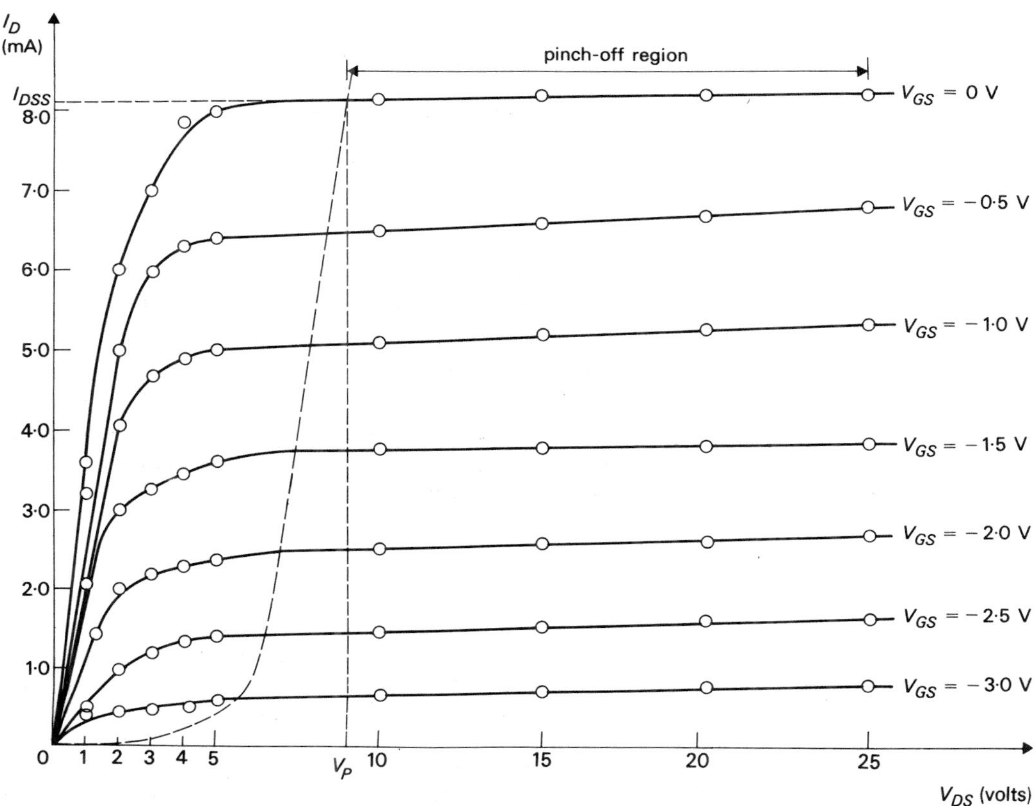

Figure 12 Output characteristic of a 2N3819 n-channel FET

It is common practice for manufacturers to quote r_{DS} when the FET i operating in the triode region, and g_{OS} when the FET is operating i the pinch-off region. In the triode region r_{DS} is small since the drain-source voltage changes very little. In the pinch-off region r_{DS} is ver large because the drain current is almost constant.

Example 1

Calculate the value of r_{DS} at constant $V_{GS}=1.5$ V

(i) in the triode region

(ii) in the pinch-off region,

for the 2N3819 n-channel FET. Use the output characteristics o Figure 12.

(i) $$r_{DS}=\frac{\text{small change in } V_{DS}}{\text{small change in } I_D} \text{ for constant } V_{GS}$$

$$r_{DS}=\frac{(1.5-0)}{(2.7-0)\times 10^{-3}}\ \Omega \text{ at } V_{GS}=-1.5 \text{ V}$$

$$=555\ \Omega \text{ (in the triode region)}$$

(ii) $$r_{DS}=\frac{(25-10)}{(3{\cdot}8-3{\cdot}76)\times 10^{-3}}\ \Omega \text{ at } V_{GS}=-1{\cdot}5 \text{ V}$$

$$=375\ \Omega \text{ (in the pinch-off region)}$$

The above results are typical for the device under test.

Transfer characteristics

The transfer characteristics of the 2N3819 n-channel FET can b plotted from the output characteristics of Figure 12. (The transfe characteristics are graphs of gate–source voltage V_{GS} against drai current I_D for constant values of drain–source voltage V_{DS}). In Figur 13, only one characteristic, at $V_{DS}=15$ V, has been drawn for clarity The characteristic is a positive slope curve which is often referred to a the *transconductance curve*. The curve approximates to a square la equation given by

$$I_D=I_{DSS}\left[1-\frac{V_{GS}}{V_P}\right]^2 \quad (1$$

where I_{DSS} is the drain saturation current
V_{GS} is the gate–source voltage
V_P is the pinch-off voltage.

The transconductance curve is very useful for determining th quiescent conditions in FET circuit design for amplifiers. Its slope a the quiescent point gives the *transconductance* g_{fs}.

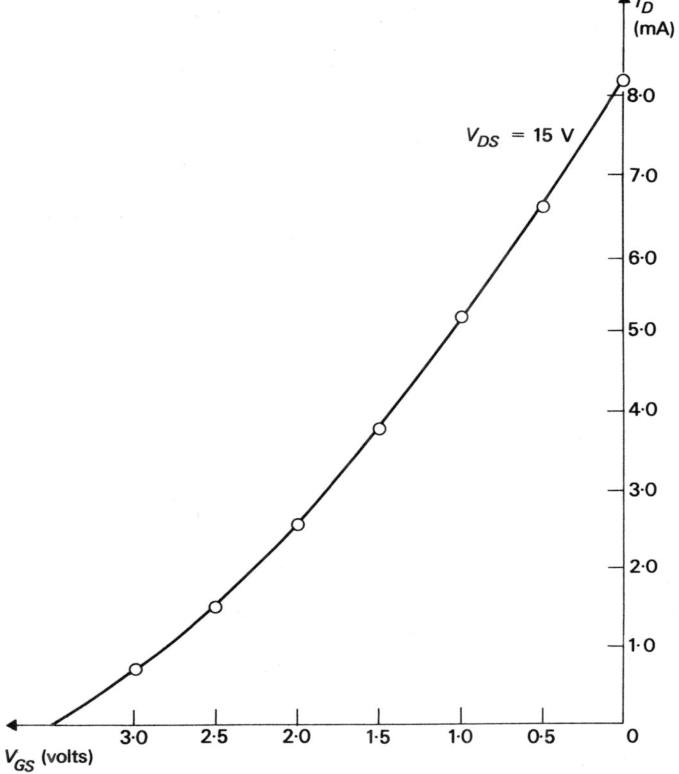

Figure 13 Transfer characteristic of a 2N3819 n-channel F E T

It can be shown by differentiating equation 1 with respect to V_{GS} that

$$\frac{dI_D}{dV_{GS}} = \frac{-2I_{DSS}}{V_P}\left[1 - \frac{V_{GS}}{V_P}\right] \tag{2}$$

The term $\frac{dI_D}{dV_{GS}}$ is one definition of the transconductance g_{fs}.

i.e. $g_{fs} = \frac{\text{small change in drain current}}{\text{small change in gate voltage}}$ for constant V_{DS}

substituting in equation 2 yields

$$g_{fs} = \frac{-2I_{DSS}}{V_P}\left[1 - \frac{V_{GS}}{V_P}\right]$$

At $V_{GS}=0$ V

$$g_{fso}=\frac{-2I_{DSS}}{V_P}$$

where g_{fso} is the transconductance when $V_{GS}=0$ V

g_{fs} is the parameter normally quoted by manufacturers in their data sheets.

FET	*bipolar transistor*	*triode valve*
low voltage gain	high voltage gain	medium voltage gain
high current gain	low current gain	high power gain
high input impedence	low input impedance	high input impedence
high output impedance	low output impedance	
low noise generation	low–medium noise generation	high noise generation
high voltage types available	low voltage types	high voltage types
characteristics are less temperature dependent than bipolar transistor	characteristics are temperature dependent	
requires an input to turn it *off*	requires zero input to turn it *off* (except for leakage)	not usually used as a switch
fast switching time operation due to absence of majority carriers	medium switching time	
exhibits the properties of a resistor and therefore highly applicable for use in integrated circuit technology	used in integrated circuits as a transistor	cannot be miniaturized
voltage controlled device	current controlled device	voltage controlled device
costlier than bipolar transistor	cheap	expensive
difficult to bias due to sample variations	easy to bias	easy to bias

Table 2 Comparison of FETs with valves and transistors

Example 2

Calculate the value of g_{fs} at constant $V_{DS}=15$ V from the transfer characteristic of Figure 13.

$$g_{fs}=\frac{\text{small change in } I_D}{\text{small change in } V_{GS}} \text{ for constant } V_{DS}$$

$$g_{fs}=\frac{(8{\cdot}15-5{\cdot}0)\times 10^{-3}}{(1{\cdot}05-0)} \text{ for } V_{DS}=15 \text{ V}$$

$$=3{\cdot}0 \text{ millisiemens}$$

The properties of an FET may now be reviewed. Table 2 compares the properties of FETs with those of the bipolar transistor and triode valve.

The input impedance of the MOSFET is even higher than that of the JUGFET because of the insulating layer. The impedance is so high that static electricity can lead to breakdown and destruction of the MOSFET. Special precautions must therefore be taken when transporting or handling MOSFETs. Manufacturer's protective devices such as conductive rubber or shorting rings should not be removed until the MOSFET has been soldered in circuit. It is good practice to earth the soldering iron tip or remove the iron from the supply just before use.

Self-assessment questions

In Questions 1–5 select the correct option.

1 Field effect transistors are unipolar devices.

TRUE/FALSE

2 There are two main types of FETs (i) JUGFETs and (ii) IGFETs.

TRUE/FALSE

3 A p-channel JUGFET is doped with a trivalent impurity which gives rise to a channel consisting of electrons.

TRUE/FALSE

4 An n-channel JUGFET is doped with a pentavalent impurity which gives rise to a channel current consisting of electrons.

TRUE/FALSE

5 The slope of the transconductance curve for an n-channel JUGFET is positive/negative.

In Questions 6–9 insert the missing word/words.

6 There are two modes of operation of FETs. These are

(i) ____________________

(ii) ____________________

7 The FET is a three terminal device. The terminals are called

(i) ____________________

(ii) ____________________

(iii) ____________________

8 The incremental channel resistance r_{DS} is defined as

$$r_{DS} = \frac{\text{small change in} \quad\quad\quad\quad}{\text{small change in} \quad\quad\quad\quad} \text{ for constant } \_\_\_\_\_\_\_\_$$

9 The transconductance g_{fs} of the FET is defined as

$$g_{fs} = \frac{\text{small change in} \quad\quad\quad\quad}{\text{small change in} \quad\quad\quad\quad} \text{ for constant } \_\_\_\_\_\_\_\_$$

10 Statement 1: The JUGFET operates only in the enhancement mode. Statement 2: The IGFET operates in both the depletion and enhancement mode.

(*a*) Only statement 1 is true
(*b*) Only statement 2 is true
(*c*) Both statements 1 and 2 are true
(*d*) Neither statement 1 nor 2 is true.
Underline the correct answer.

11 Sketch the output characteristics of an n-channel JUGFET and indicate on the characteristics
(i) the triode region
(ii) the pinch-off region
(iii) the breakdown region.

In Questions 12 and 13 insert the missing word(s).

12 For an n-channel JUGFET to operate, the drain voltage needs to be ____________ with respect to the source.

13 For an n-channel JUGFET to operate, the gate voltage needs to be _____________ with respect to the source.

14 Statement 1: An n-channel depletion mode MOSFET is normally an *on* device requiring a reverse gate voltage to turn it *off*.
Statement 2: A p-channel enhancement mode MOSFET is normally an *off* device requiring a forward gate voltage to turn it *on*.

(*a*) Only statement 1 is true
(*b*) Only statement 2 is true
(*c*) Both statements 1 and 2 are true
(*d*) Neither statement 1 or 2 is true.
Underline the correct answer.

15 Statement 1: r_{DS} is small when the FET is operating in the triode region since the drain–source voltage changes by small amounts.
Statement 2: r_{DS} is large when the FET is operating in the pinch-off region since the drain current is very nearly constant.

(*a*) Only statement 1 is true
(*b*) Only statement 2 is true
(*c*) Both statements 1 and 2 are true
(*d*) Neither statement 1 nor 2 is true.
Underline the correct answer.

16 Match the properties labelled (*a*) to (*m*) with the three devices labelled 1, 2 and 3 by placing the appropriate letters next to the device. Each letter may be used once, more than once or not at all.

(1) FET	(*a*) high input impedance
	(*b*) low input impedance
(2) Triode valve	(*c*) low voltage gain
	(*d*) high voltage gain
(3) Bipolar transistor	(*e*) fast switching time
	(*f*) medium switching time
	(*g*) voltage controlled device
	(*h*) current controlled device
	(*j*) expensive
	(*k*) cheap
	(*l*) difficult to bias
	(*m*) easy to bias

17 State two precautions which need to be taken when soldering MOSFETs in circuit.

Solutions to self-assessment questions (pages 21–23)

1 TRUE

2 TRUE

3 FALSE. A p-channel JUGFET is doped with a trivalent impurity which gives rise to a channel current consisting of holes.

4 TRUE

5 Positive.

6 (i) Enhancement.
(ii) Depletion.

7 (i) Gate.
(ii) Drain.
(iii) Source.

8 $r_{DS} = \dfrac{\text{small change in } V_{DS}}{\text{small change in } I_D}$

for constant V_{GS}

9 $g_{fs} = \dfrac{\text{small change in } I_D}{\text{small change in } V_{GS}}$

for constant V_{DS}.

10 The correct answer is (*b*). Statement 1 should read: The JUGFET operates only in the depletion mode.

11 See Figure 12.

12 Positive.

13 Negative.

14 The correct answer is (*a*). Statement 2 should read: A p-channel enhancement mode MOSFET is a normally *off* device requiring a reverse gate voltage to turn it *on*.

15 The correct answer is (*c*). Both sta ments are true.

16 (1) FET
(*a*) (*c*) (*e*) (*g*) (*k*) (*l*)
(2) Triode valve
(*a*) (*g*) (*j*) (*m*)
(3) Bipolar transistor
(*b*) (*d*) (*f*) (*h*) (*k*) (*m*)

17
(*a*) The conductive rubber or shorti rings should not be removed un the MOSFET has been soldered circuit.
(*b*) The soldering iron tip should earthed or removed from the supp whilst the MOSFET is being so dered in circuit.

After reading the following material, the reader shall:

2 Describe the circuit applications of FETs.
2.1 Describe the common biasing methods employed in the FE common source amplifier.
2.2 Describe the circuit of an FET common source amplifier having resistive load.
2.3 Calculate the stage gain of an FET common source amplifier having resistive load.
2.4 Describe the effect on the frequency response of adding an inductiv load to the circuit of **2.2.**
2.5 Describe the performance of a common source amplifier with
(*a*) an inductive load
(*b*) a tuned circuit load.
2.6 State the use and advantages of the FET as a switch.

Like the bipolar transistor and triode valve, the field effect transisto is a three terminal device. Three modes of connection are possibl
(i) the common source
(ii) the common gate, and
(iii) the common drain (or source follower).

Figure 14 illustrates the three modes of connection of the FET bipolar transistor and triode valve. There are similarities betwee similar modes – for example common cathode, common source an common emitter. Amplifier characteristics for the three devices i their three modes are similar. Characteristics such as input an

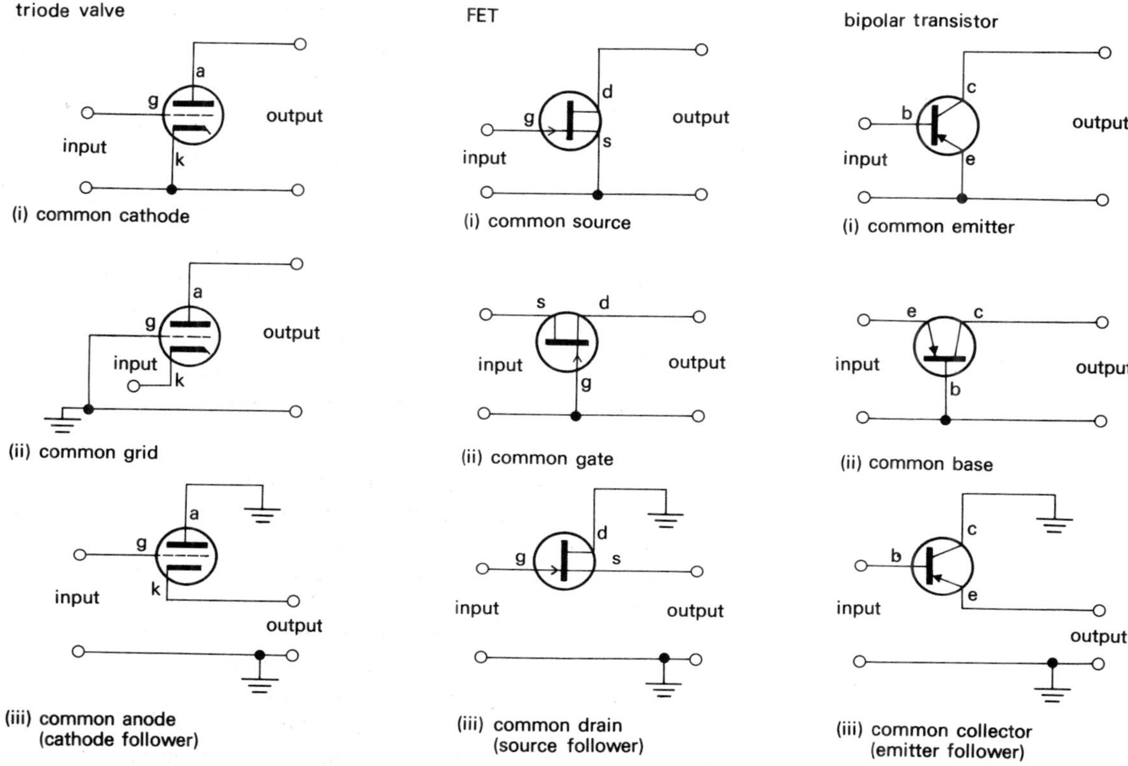

Figure 14 Comparison of the three modes of connection of the triode valve, bipolar transistor and field effect transistor

output impedance, voltage gain, current gain and transfer characteristics have already been discussed in Electronics 2 for the bipolar transistor and triode valve. Similar characteristics have been included in the preceding section of this book for the FET.

Due to its high input impedance, the common source mode of connection is used in audio amplifiers and in high input impedance amplifiers found in oscilloscopes and valve voltmeters. The high input impedance feature is lost in the common gate mode. This mode is therefore used in high frequency circuits and in matching circuits where a low input impedance needs to be matched to a high input impedance. The common drain mode of connection has a high input impedance and a low output impedance, and is therefore used in buffer amplifiers.

There are large variations in the characteristics of FETs from sample to sample, and hence the biasing of FETs must be done individually. As with the bipolar transistor common emitter amplifier (see topic area Small signal amplifiers in Electronics 2), the FET common source amplifier needs to be biased at a suitable quiescent value. The most obvious way to bias the FET is using two separate batteries, a shown in Figure 15(*a*). However, this method is rarely used because does not tolerate large sample variations.

Figure 15(*b*) shows how the bias circuits can operate from a single d. supply. The voltage drop across the source resistor R_S, due to th source current, provides the necessary reverse bias on the gate–sourc resistor R_G. So that there is no appreciable voltage across the gate source resistor, its ohmic value is usually chosen to be less than th input resistance of the FET. If for any reason the drain curren increases, the source voltage increases. The gate is thus more negativ with respect to the source, which tends to compensate for the increas in the drain current. The amount of compensation depends on th value of R_S which should be large. Unfortunately a large value of R reduces the quiescent current.

Figure 15(*c*) shows the most common biasing circuit. It has improve stability performance over that of Figure 15(*b*) . Resistors R_1 and R form a potential divider circuit which provides the necessary bia voltage V_{GS}. R_S and C_S serve the same function as the emitter resisto and emitter capacitor in the bipolar transistor common emitte amplifier, namely to provide good stability (see topic area Feedback and prevent reduction of the signal gain. Capacitor C_1 couples th input signal to the gate of the FET, and capacitor C_2 couples th output signal to the next stage. The price paid for a stabilize quiescent current is that more of the supply voltage is dropped acros R_S. Inversion of the input signal occurs at the output. This is due to positive voltage increment at the input causing the drain current i_d t increase. This, in turn, increases the drain resistor voltage $i_d R_L$ an hence the output voltage decreases.

The circuits of Figure 15(*b*) and (*c*) may be analysed to determine th circuit characteristics. One method of analysis is by the use of a equivalent circuit. An equivalent circuit is an electrical network whic represents the performance of the active device and its associate circuitry. Figure 16(*a*) illustrates the complete equivalent circuit of th FET common source voltage amplifier of Figure 15(*c*). At the mid band frequencies the reactances of the coupling capacitor C_2 and th interelectrode capacitances can be neglected because the effect o frequency is not so pronounced. The gate input resistances r_{GS} and r_G are usually very high and can also be neglected. This results in th simplified equivalent circuit shown in Figure 16(*b*).

Using this equivalent circuit:

$$v_{out} = -i_d R_L{}^1 \text{ where } R_L{}^1 \text{ is the value of } R_L \text{ and } r_{DS} \text{ in parallel}$$

$$= -g_{fs} v_{gs} \left(\frac{r_{DS} R_L}{r_{DS} + R_L} \right)$$

$$v_{in} = v_{gs}$$

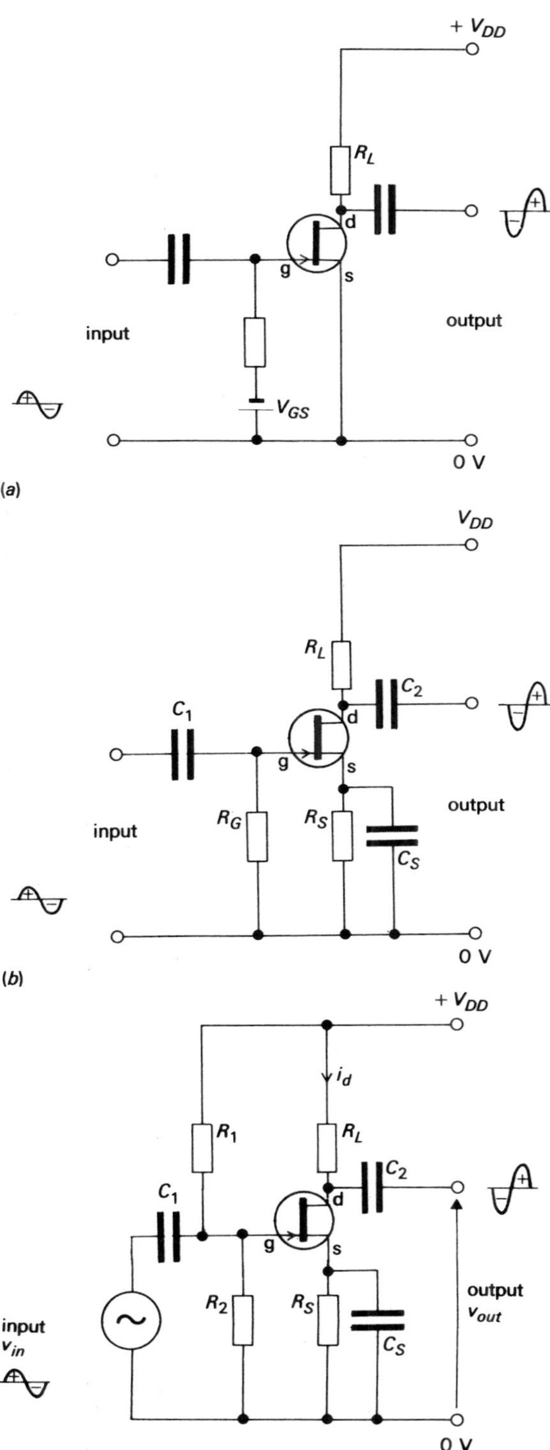

gure 15 Common biasing methods for an FET common source amplifier
(a) biased from two supplies
(b) biased from a single supply
(c) biased with temperature-stabilized circuit

$$\text{Voltage gain} = A_v = \frac{v_{\text{out}}}{v_{\text{in}}}$$

$$= \frac{-g_{fs}v_{gs}\left(\dfrac{r_{DS}R_L}{r_{DS}+R_L}\right)}{v_{gs}}$$

i.e $A_v = -g_{fs}\left(\dfrac{r_{DS}R_L}{r_{DS}+R_L}\right)$

The negative sign indicates the inversion between input and outpu voltages.

If $R_L \ll r_{DS}$, $A_v = -g_{fs}R_L$(which is similar to $-g_mR_L$ for a triode valve

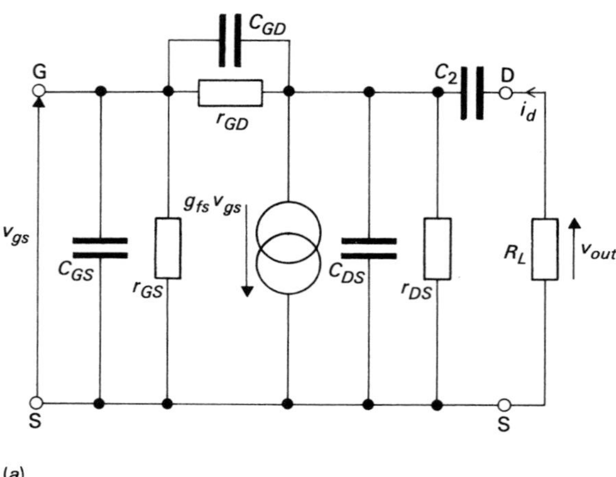

(a)

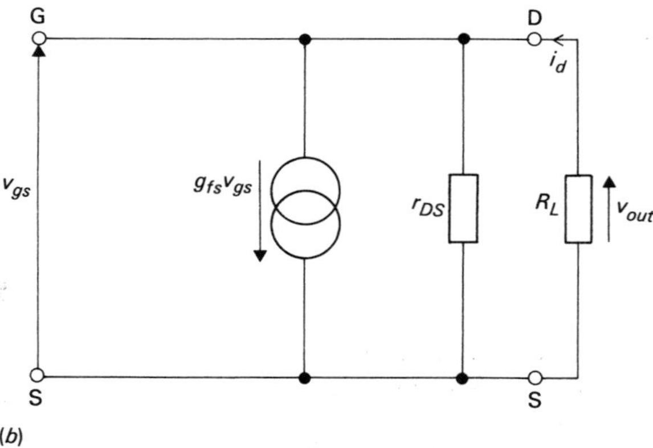

(b)

Figure 16 FET common source amplifier equivalent circuits
(a) complete constant current equivalent circuit
(b) simplified constant current equivalent circuit

Example 3

An n-channel FET is connected as a simple amplifier as shown in Figure 15(*c*). When $g_{fs}=1{\cdot}2$ mS and $r_{DS}=47$ kΩ at the operating point, and $R_L=56$ kΩ, determine the voltage gain of the stage.

Here $R_L \ll r_{DS}$ cannot be applied

$$A_v = -1{\cdot}2\times10^{-3}\frac{47\times10^3\times56\times10^3}{103\times10^3}$$

$$A_v = -30{\cdot}7$$

If this result is compared with the voltage gain of a bipolar transistor it can be seen that the voltage gain of an FET is small compared with that of the bipolar transistor. Also the power gain of an FET is extremely large because the current gain is high.

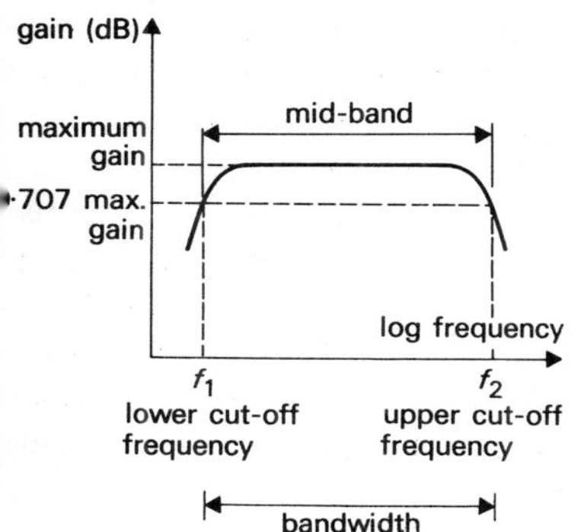

Figure 17 Frequency response curve of an amplifier

It was stated in Electronics 2 (topic area Small signal amplifiers) that when the power gain of an amplifier falls to half the constant or mid-band value, the bandwidth or passband of an amplifier is defined as f_2-f_1 (the difference between the upper and lower cut-off frequencies), i.e.

bandwidth = upper cut-off frequency − lower cut-off frequency
bandwidth $= f_2 - f_1$

Figure 17 illustrates the frequency response of the typical FET common source amplifier of Figure 15(*c*). The upper and lower cut-off frequencies and the bandwidth of the amplifier are indicated on the frequency response curve.

For many applications e.g. oscilloscope and video amplifiers, a wide bandwidth accompanied by a high gain is necessary. Unfortunately, the two cannot be obtained simultaneously, because as the bandwidth increases the gain decreases due to the effect of frequency on reactance. In order to extend the bandwidth of an amplifier, either the upper or lower cut-off frequency can be extended. It is more usual to extend the upper cut-off frequency.

Figure 18 illustrates the equivalent circuit of the FET common source amplifier operating at high frequencies. The effect of the drain–source capacitance C_{DS} cannot now be neglected.

One way of increasing the upper cut-off frequency is to decrease the value of R_L^1 i.e. reduce the value of the drain resistor R_L. This method however increases the upper cut-off frequency at the expense of gain.

A better method of increasing the upper cut-off frequency with less reduction of gain is by the addition of a small series inductor to the drain load resistor (Figure 19(*a*)). The circuit is commonly called a *shunt peaking* circuit. The capacitance C_{DS} effectively appears across

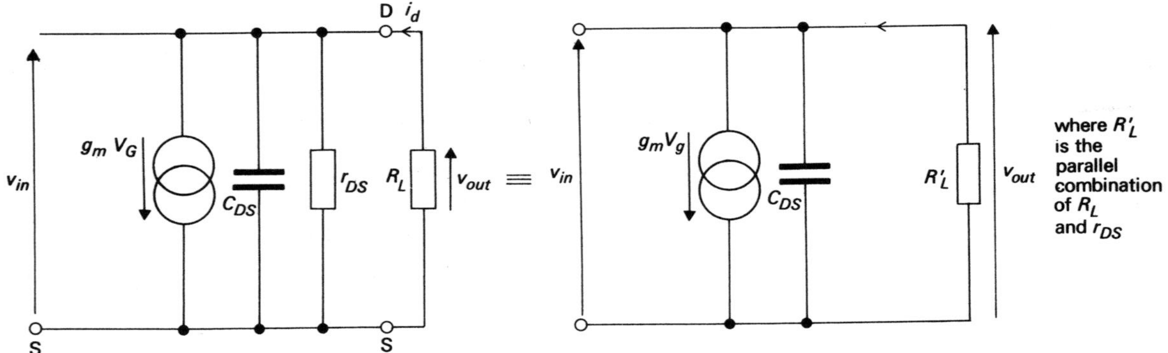

Figure 18 High frequency equivalent circuit of FET common source amplifier

the series combination of L and R_L, the impedance of the load now being a series/parallel circuit as shown in Figure 19(*b*). There is a marked reduction in the effect of C_{DS} on the frequency response curve of the amplifier. The effect of the series inductor is to increase the output impedance at the high frequency end of the frequency response curve. The increase in output impedance tends to compensate for the decreasing reactance of C_{DS}. The effect of adding the series inductor is shown on the frequency response curve of Figure 19(*c*). This method of increasing the amplifier bandwidth is used in wideband or video amplifiers, the upper cut-off frequency of these amplifiers being typically in the order of megahertz.

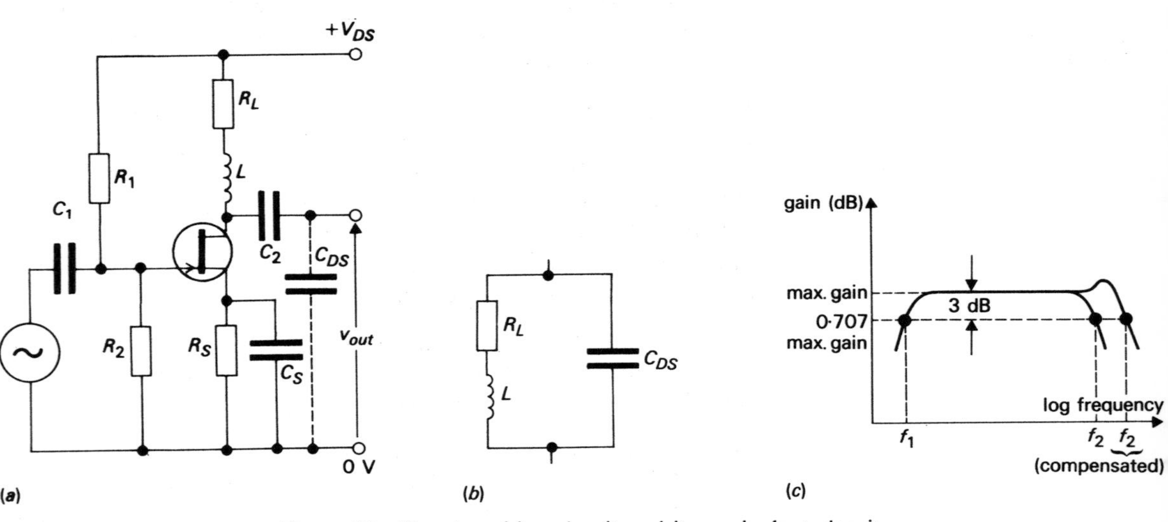

Figure 19 Shunt peaking circuit and its equivalent circuit
(a) common source shunt peaking circuit
(b) equivalent circuit for load
(c) the effect on the frequency response curve illustrating high frequency compensation

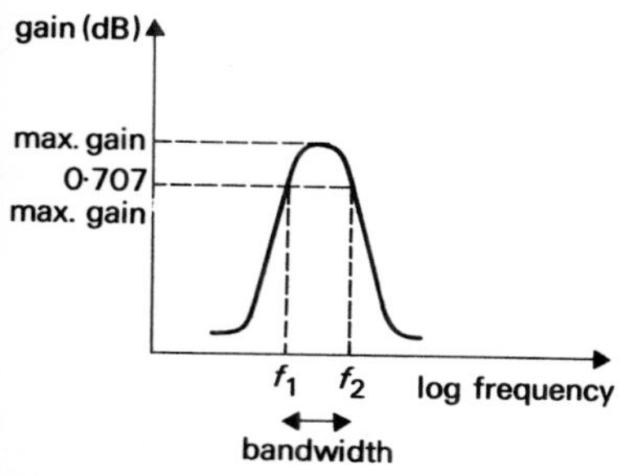

Figure 20 Frequency response of an r.f. amplifier

The common source amplifier with an inductive load or a tuned circuit load is recognizable as a radio frequency amplifier. These amplifiers are designed for the narrow band of frequencies within the r.f. spectrum and they thus have a narrow bandwidth (see Figure 20). In order to achieve such a response, a frequency sensitive load is required and a tuned circuit is usually employed. The amplifier increases the signal output and it does so without increasing the signal noise, i.e. the signal to noise ratio is improved (see topic area Noise). Such amplifiers are generally employed in v.h.f./u.h.f. receivers for radio and television.

Figure 21 shows a typical common source r.f. amplifier employing an inductive load L_2. L_1 is tuned to the resonant frequency by the parallel capacitor C_1, the signal being applied to the gate of the FET. The source resistor R_S and capacitor C_S provide the same function as in the small signal amplifier described earlier. The output is taken from the load transformer L_2.

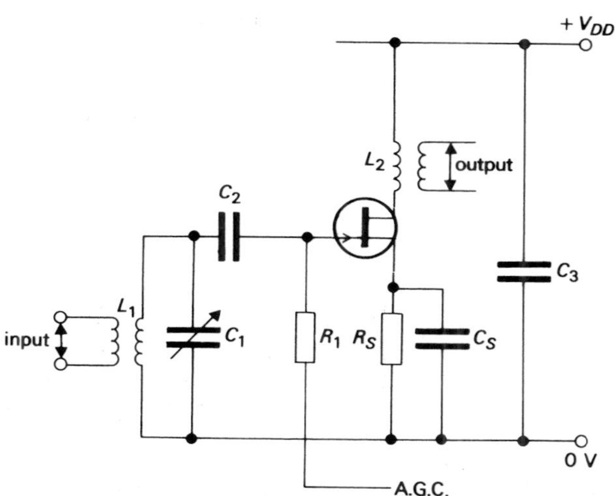

Figure 21 Common source r.f. amplifier with an inductive load

Figure 22 shows a typical common source r.f. amplifier employing a tuned circuit load. Frequency tuning of the output can be achieved by either a variable inductor or capacitor. Variable capacitor tuning is the more common. The resonant frequency f_0 of the parallel tuned circuit of Figure 22 is given by the expression

$$f_0 = \frac{1}{2\pi}\sqrt{\left(\frac{1}{LC} - \frac{R^2}{L^2}\right)}$$

or if R is small

$$f_0 = \frac{1}{2\pi\sqrt{(LC)}}$$

and the Q factor, $Q_0 = \frac{2\pi f_0 L}{R} = \frac{\omega_0 L}{R}$

The equivalent circuit of the tuned circuit load r.f. amplifier is shown in Figure 23(a).

When designing tuned circuit amplifiers it is convenient to simplify the tuned circuit series coil resistance R into an equivalent parallel resistance R_p as shown in Figure 23(b).

The complete equivalent circuit can now be drawn as shown in Figure 23(c).

Input voltage, $v_{\text{in}} = v_{gs}$

Output voltage, $v_{\text{out}} = -g_{fs} v_{gs} \left(\frac{R_p r_{DS}}{R_p + r_{DS}} \right)$

The impedance of the loss free tuned circuit at resonance is infinite and does not appear therefore in the final expression

$$\therefore \text{voltage gain} = -g_{fs} \left(\frac{R_p r_{DS}}{R_p + r_{DS}} \right)$$

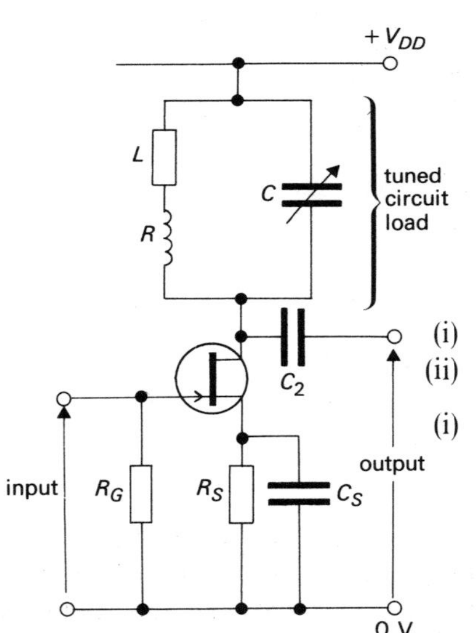

Figure 22 Common source r.f. amplifier with a tuned circuit load

Example 4

In the circuit of Figure 22 the tuned circuit load has a high Q coil with an inductance of 1 mH and a capacitance of 1000 pF. The Q factor at the resonant frequency is 100. If the FET parameters have values of $r_{DS} = 250\ \text{k}\Omega$ and $g_{fs} = 2$ mS, determine

(i) the resonant frequency of the tuned circuit
(ii) the voltage gain of the circuit at this frequency.

(i) $f_0 = \frac{1}{2\pi\sqrt{(LC)}}$ as for a high Q coil $\omega^2 L^2 \gg R^2$

$$\therefore f_0 = \frac{1}{2\pi\sqrt{(1 \times 10^{-3} \times 1000 \times 10^{-12})}} \text{ hertz}$$

$$= \frac{1}{2\pi\sqrt{10^{-12}}}$$

$$= \frac{10^6}{2\pi}$$

$$= 159 \text{ kHz}$$

(iii) $\text{Voltage gain} = -g_{fs}\left(\frac{R_p r_{DS}}{R_p + r_{DS}}\right)$

$$R_p = \omega_0 L Q_0 = 2\pi f_0 L Q_0$$

$$= 2\pi \times \frac{10^6}{2\pi} \times 1 \times 10^{-3} \times 100$$

$$= 100 \text{ k}\Omega$$

$$\therefore \text{Voltage gain} = -2 \times 10^{-3}\left(\frac{100 \times 10^3 \times 250 \times 10^3}{100 \times 10^3 + 250 \times 10^3}\right)$$

$$= -2 \times 10^{-3}\left(\frac{25 \times 10^9}{350 \times 10^3}\right)$$

$$= -143$$

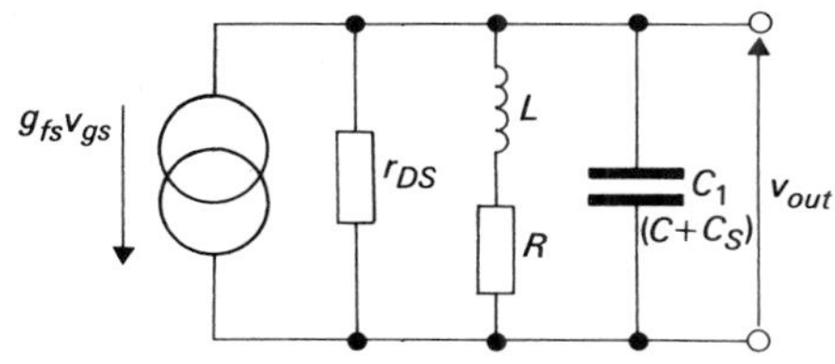

(*a*)

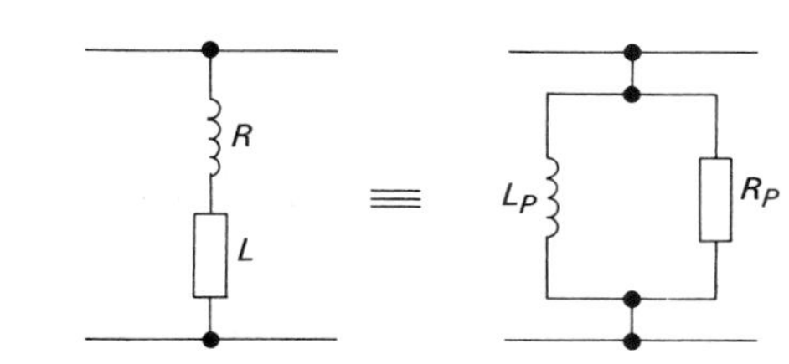

(*b*)

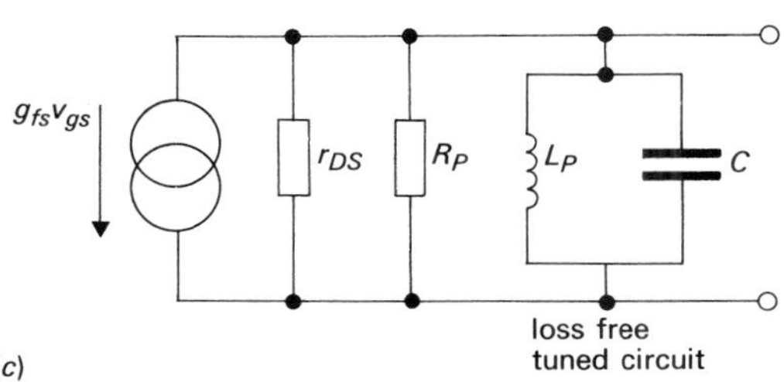

(*c*)

Figure 23 Common source r.f. amplifier equivalent circuit
(a) complete equivalent circuit
(b) equivalent circuit of tuned circuit
(c) equivalent circuit with series coil resistance replaced by its equivalent parallel resistance

The FET as a switch

An ideal switch has *zero* resistance when *on* and *infinite* resistanc when *off* (see topic area Logic elements and circuits in Electronics 2

From Figure 12, for an n-channel FET it can be seen that th incremental channel resistance r_{DS} is a function of both V_{GS} and V_{D} When V_{GS} is negative the FET is switched off and r_{DS} is extremely higl being typically 10^{12} Ω. When $V_{GS}=0$ V the FET is switched on and r is quite small, being typically about 15 Ω. Figure 12 also shows th characteristics passing through the origin; there is no *offset voltage* fc an FET. The *on*/*off* time for an FET is determined by both th external circuitry and the interelectrode capacitances. Unlike bipol transistors, FETs have no minority charge carriers stored in th channel, and this gives rise to fast switching speeds.

The FET is thus an ideal switching device having

(i) a low resistance in the *on* state and a high resistance in the *off* sta
(ii) zero offset voltage, and
(iii) fast turn on and turn off times.

These three characteristics of the FET make it ideal as a switch in th design of chopper amplifiers, analogue switches and sample and ho circuits in analogue memories.

Self-assessment questions

18 Match the properties labelled (*a*) to (*d*) with the three modes connection of the FET labelled 1, 2 and 3 by placing the appropria letter(s) in the space adjacent to the three modes.

(1) common gate	(*a*) low input resistance
(2) common source	(*b*) high input resistance
(3) common drain	(*c*) low output resistance
	(*d*) high output resistance

Each letter may be used once, more than once or not at all.

19 Sketch circuit diagrams showing how the FET can be connected
(i) the common source mode
(ii) the common gate mode
(iii) the common drain mode.

In questions 20–22 select the correct options.

20 In an n-channel FET common source amplifier, a negative voltag increment at the input causes the output voltage to increase/decreas

21 The output voltage from a common source amplifier is phase shifte by 180° from the input voltage.

TRUE/FALS

22 An FET common source amplifier employing a tuned circuit load is a wideband/radio frequency amplifier.

23 The voltage gain A_v of a common source amplifier with a resistive load is given by the expression

$A_v =$ (assume R_L is not less than r_{DS})

24 List three methods of increasing the upper cut-off frequency of a common source amplifier.

25 List three properties of the FET which make it an ideal switching device.

26 Sketch the simplified equivalent circuit of an FET common source amplifier at the mid-band frequencies.

27 What is the purpose of the shunt peaking circuit in an FET wideband or video amplifier?

28 Sketch the circuit diagram of an FET common source r.f. amplifier.

29 Give two examples where the FET is used as a switch.

30 An FET is connected as a simple common source amplifier as shown in Figure 15(*c*). If $g_{fs} = 2$ mS and $r_{DS} = 56$ kΩ at the operating point and $R_L = 100$ kΩ, determine the voltage gain of the amplifier stage.

31 Give one example of where the FET common source r.f. amplifier is to be found.

32 Sketch the circuit diagram of a small signal FET common source amplifier with temperature stability, indicating the function of each component.

Solutions to self-assessment questions (pages 34–35)

18 (1) Common gate (*a*) (*d*)
(2) Common source (*b*) (*d*)
(3) Common drain (*b*) (*c*)

19 See Figure 14.

20 Increase.

21 FALSE. The output voltage is phase inverted from the input voltage.

22 Radio frequency.

23 $A_v = -g_{fs}\left(\frac{r_{DS}R_L}{r_{DS}+R_L}\right)$

24 Three methods of increasing the upper cut-off frequency of a common source amplifier are
(i) decrease the ohmic value of the drain resistor
(ii) use a shunt peaking circuit in the drain circuit
(iii) apply negative feedback.

25 The FET is an ideal switching device because it has:
(i) low resistance when *on*, high resistance when *off*
(ii) zero offset voltage
(iii) fast turn on and turn off times.

26 See Figure 16(*b*).

27 The purpose of the shunt peaking circuit is to increase the bandwidth of an amplifier for utilization as a wideband amplifier.

28 See Figure 21.

29 Examples of where the FET is used as a switch include:
(i) chopper amplifiers
(ii) analogue switches
(iii) sample and hold circuits.
(any two are correct)

30 $A_v = -g_{fs}\left(\frac{r_{DS}R_L}{r_{DS}+R_L}\right)$

$$= -2\times 10^{-3}\left(\frac{56\times 10^3\times 100\times 1}{156\times 10^3}\right.$$

$$= -2\times\frac{56\times 100}{156}$$

$$\approx -72$$

31 The FET common source r.f. amplifier is used in a v.h.f./u.h.f. receive for radio or television.

32 See Figure 15(*c*). The function c each component is:

R_1, R_2 are biasing resistors
R_L is the load resistor
R_S is the temperature stabilization resistor
C_1 is a decoupling capacitor
C_2 is a coupling capacitor
C_S is the source bypass capacitor.

Topic area Amplifiers

After reading the following material the reader shall:

3 Understand the performance of small signal amplifiers.
3.1 State the biasing conditions for class A, B, AB and C operation.
3.2 List the main applications of each type of amplifier in **3.1.**
3.3 Describe the single stage
(*a*) audio frequency amplifier
(*b*) radio frequency amplifier
(*c*) wideband amplifier
(*d*) buffer amplifier (emitter follower).
3.4 State the functions of individual components present in an r.f. amplifier.
3.5 Explain the selectivity of a tuned amplifier.
3.6 State the applications of buffer amplifiers.

The amplifier is probably the most common electronic circuit. It is used in radio and television receivers as a small signal amplifier and in battery operated equipment such as car radios and hearing aids as a large signal amplifier. There are many different types of amplifier, for example audio amplifiers, radio frequency amplifiers, video amplifiers, buffer amplifiers and so on, and these reflect the large number of uses to which the amplifier is put. These uses include wideband amplifiers in oscilloscopes and radar equipment, buffer amplifiers in power supplies and transmitters, differential amplifiers in integrated circuits, radio frequency amplifiers in radios and audio amplifiers in hi-fi equipment. The uses are by no means exhausted; further uses may be found in the following text. The purpose of an amplifier is to increase the amplitude of the voltage or current or power of an electrical signal.

When an amplifier is used to amplify either the voltage or current of an input signal such that the output signal is not distorted it is said to be a small signal amplifier. The parameters of the device are assumed to remain constant during the period of operation of the device.

(Parameter is a word now used to represent any term that aids description of how a device (or system) behaves within quoted boundaries. For instance, some of the parameters of resistance wire are length, diameter, and resistivity.)

When an amplifier is used to amplify the power of an input signal it is said to be a large signal amplifier. The parameters of the device are not constant during the period of operation of the device.

A simple example of this is the audio power amplifier where maximum power at audio frequencies is transferred from a small signal voltage amplifier to a loudspeaker driven by a power amplifier.

Terminology associated with amplifiers

1 The *gain* of an amplifier is the amount of increase of the output signal amplitude compared with the amplitude of the signal before amplification.

This definition takes into account the total waveform of the output which includes the a.c. and d.c. component. If just the a.c. component of the output waveform is considered, another way of defining the gain for a varying input waveform is given by

$$\text{gain} = \frac{\text{change in output signal}}{\text{corresponding change in input signal}}$$

The amount of amplification depends on:

(i) the number of stages used
(ii) the design of the amplifier stage
(iii) the characteristics of the device used in the amplifier stage.

2 If the *frequency* of an input signal (of constant amplitude) to an amplifier is varied and the gain recorded, a graph can be plotted of gain against frequency. The most convenient scales for the axes are chosen as required, the gain being measured as a ratio, or plotted on a logarithmic scale in dB (decibels). The way in which the gain varies with frequency gives an indication of the frequency response of an amplifier. A typical graph is shown in Figure 24.

When the power gain of an amplifier falls to half the constant or mid-band value, the bandwidth or passband of the amplifier is defined as $f_2 - f_1$ (the difference between the upper and lower cut-off frequencies). Another way of expressing bandwidth is to identify the frequencies where the gain falls by 3 dB, as shown below:

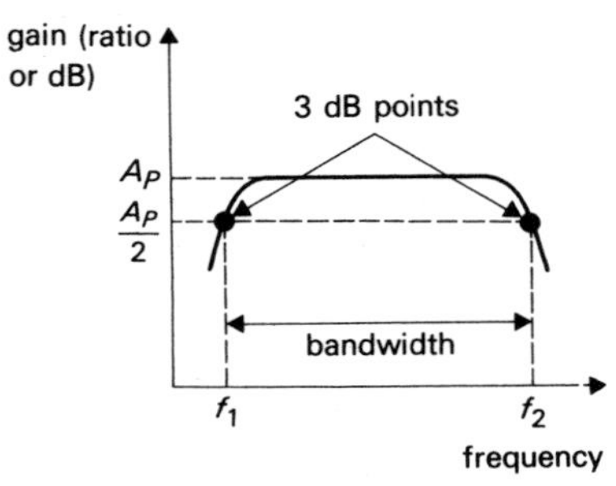

Figure 24 Frequency response of an amplifier

$$\text{power ratio (dB)} = 10 \log_{10}\left(\frac{P_1}{P_2}\right) \quad (1 \text{ dB} = 0{\cdot}1 \text{ B})$$

If the two power levels P_1 and P_2 are produced in resistors R_1 and R_2 respectively by voltages V_1 and V_2 respectively,

$$\text{power ratio} = 10 \log_{10}\left[\frac{V_1{}^2/R_2}{V_2{}^2/R_1}\right] \text{ dB}$$

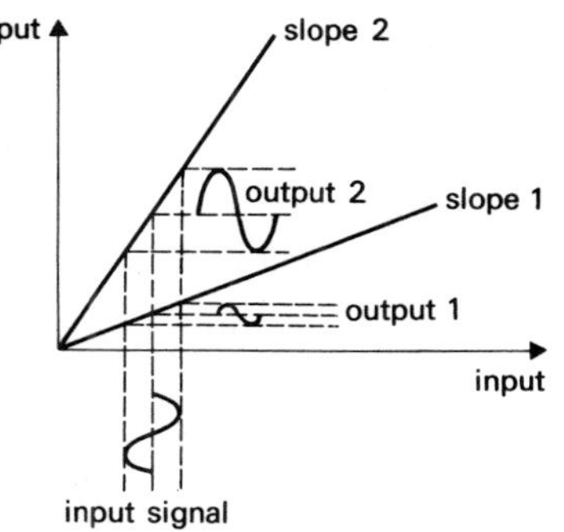

Figure 25 Theoretical transfer characteristic

Assuming the resistances are equal i.e. $R_1 = R_2 = R$ (this is strictly not true in electronic circuits, since the two voltages V_1 and V_2 may be developed across unequal input and load resistors in an amplifier circuit),

$$\text{power ratio} = 10 \log_{10}\left[\frac{V_1^{\,2}}{V_2^{\,2}}\right] \text{ dB}$$

$$= 20 \log_{10}\left[\frac{V_1}{V_2}\right] \text{ dB}$$

When the gain or power ratio falls to one-half of its original value then $V_2 = 0{\cdot}707 V_1$ and

$$\text{power ratio (power loss)} = 20 \log_{10}\left(\frac{1}{0{\cdot}707}\right) \text{ dB}$$

$$= 20 \log_{10} 1{\cdot}414$$
$$= 20 \times 0{\cdot}150$$
$$= 3{\cdot}01 \text{ dB}$$

which for practical purposes may be taken to be 3 dB. The 3 dB points are illustrated on the frequency response curve of Figure 24.

3 The *transfer characteristic* of an amplifier indicates the amount of gain that may be obtained from an amplifying device. This can be seen from the graph of output signal against input signal shown in Figure 25.

It can be seen that the steeper the slope the greater the amplification. In practice the slope is nonlinear and hence the output can be severely distorted unless careful design is used, as shown in Figure 26.

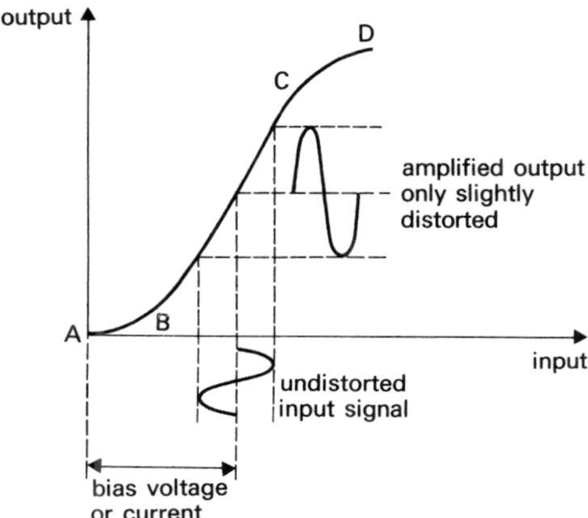

Figure 26 Transfer characteristic of a typical amplifying device

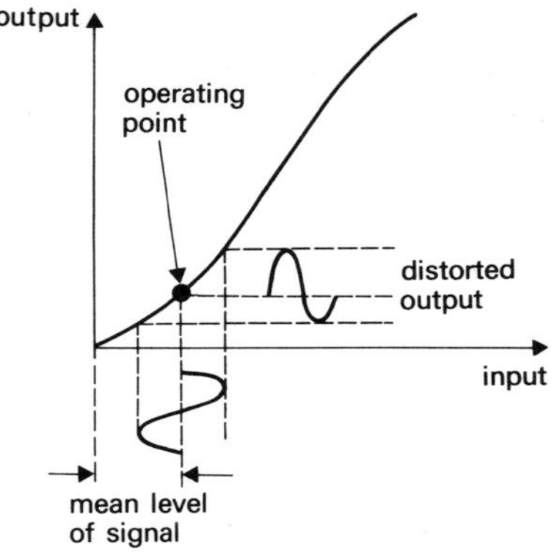

Figure 27 Distortion using non-linear part of transfer characteristic

By positioning the mean level of the input signal on the most linear part of the curve the amount of distortion produced is minimized.

The position of the input signal mean level on the most linear part of the curve is achieved by biasing, about which more information can be found in topic area Small signal amplifiers in Electronics 2.

From Figure 24 the amplifier can be considered to be a filter that passes only a band of approximately constant amplitude signals between frequencies f_2 and f_1. Outside this band of frequencies the amplitude of the signals passed decreases rapidly. Hence an input signal that contains frequencies outside this passband cannot be reproduced exactly at the output of the amplifier, because signals outside the passband are amplified at values different from those inside the passband. This causes distortion of the output signal, known as *frequency distortion.* This distortion can be reduced using feedback as shown in topic area Feedback.

Consider Figure 27 where the input signal is applied at the point shown. The output is grossly distorted because the operating point is not on the most linear part of the curve. This causes distortion of the output signal known as *amplitude distortion.*

It can also be seen that if the operating point is at the centre part of the curve and the input signal has too large an amplitude, amplitude distortion occurs. This distortion can be minimized by choosing the most linear part of the characteristic, and by restricting the amplitude of the input signal to the lowest acceptable value.

Classes of bias

Whenever active devices, e.g. transistors and valves, are used in amplifying circuits they are classified according to the selection of the operating or quiescent point. There are several classes of bias; the most common are class A, class B, class AB and class C.

Figure 28 illustrates the four common classes of bias for a bipolar transistor. In class A the transistor is biased at the mid-point on the linear part of the output characteristics, i.e. saturation and cut-off are avoided. The output is thus a faithful replica of the input and no distortion occurs. Current exists in the amplifier load during the complete cycle of the input signal. In the absence of an input signal, power is still dissipated in the transistor since the device is biased *on.*

There is thus a possibility of thermal runaway occurring in transistor amplifiers. The efficiency of class A bias is low – theoretically it cannot exceed 50 per cent. Class A bias is normally useful only for low power (less than 2 W) small signal audio frequency amplifiers, as found in car radios and portable pocket radios.

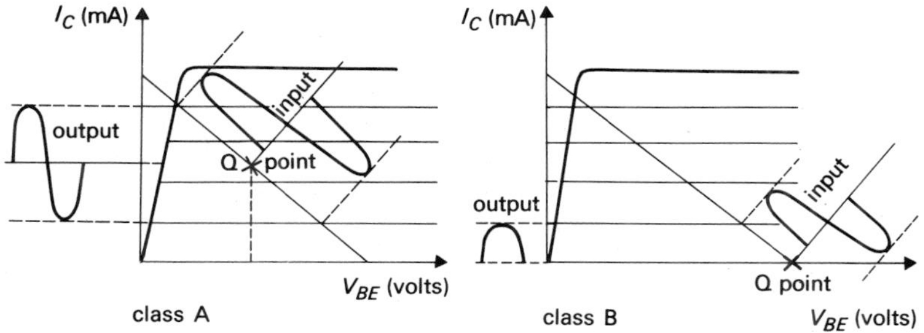

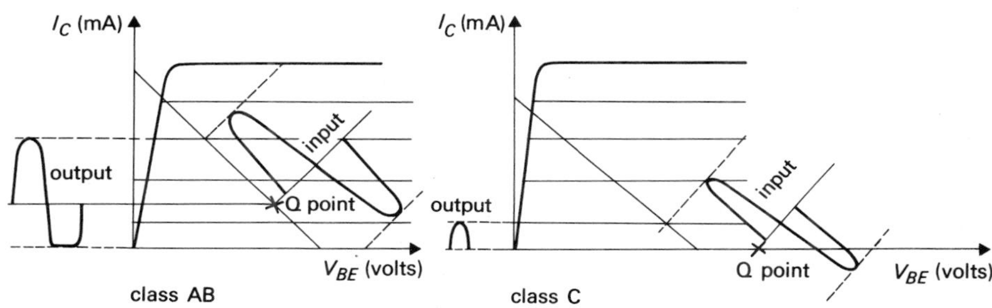

Figure 28 The classes of bias in transistor amplifiers

A much higher output power and efficiency can be obtained by operating the transistor in class B, where the transistor is biased at the cut-off point. Consequently distortion must occur on one half cycle since current exists in the amplifier load only during the other half cycle of the input signal. The distortion can be overcome by operating two transistors with class B bias in push-pull (see Objective 4.1 in topic area Amplifiers). Class B bias is usually used in audio power amplifiers and in some tuned radio frequency amplifiers.

Class AB is a combination of class A and class B, i.e. the bias point lies somewhere between the mid-point and the cut-off point. Current therefore exists in the amplifier load for more than one half cycle but less than the complete cycle of the input signal. Consequently class AB has a greater output power and efficiency than class A, and less distortion than class B. Class AB is therefore used in audio power amplifiers.

In class C operation the transistor is biased beyond cut-off; current exists in the amplifier load for less than one half of the input signal. Consequently class C amplifiers have a very high efficiency, but suffer from a very high distortion. They are used in tuned radio frequency power amplifiers and in oscillator circuits (since in class C the active device is acting as a switch). The operation of a class C amplifier in oscillator circuits is discussed in a later topic area of this book.

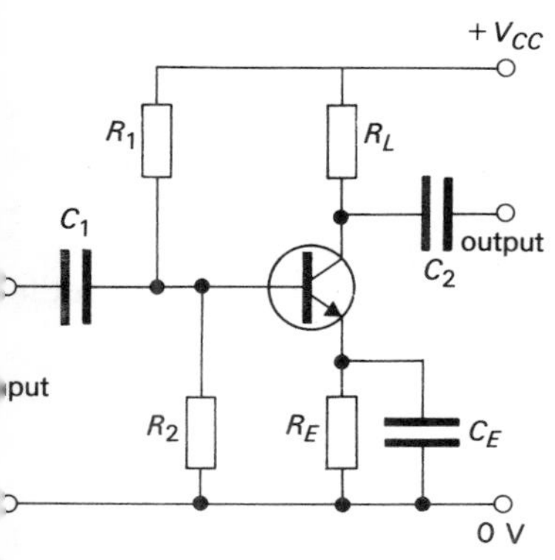

igure 29 Typical circuit for a ngle stage audio amplifier (class A)

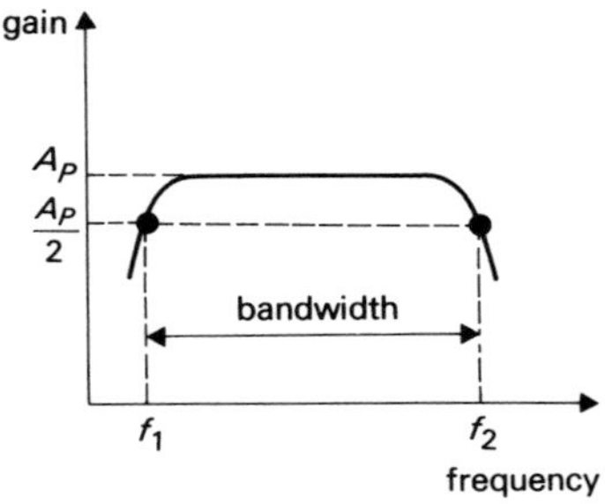

audio amplifier type	f_1 (Hz)	f_2 (kHz)	bandwidth (kHz)
communi-cations audio amplifier (telephone)	300	3·4	3·1
LW/MW broadcast receiver audio amplifier	150	8	7·85
f.m. receiver audio amplifier	100	15	14·9
hi-fi audio amplifier	30	30	29·97

Figure 30 Frequency response of a single stage audio amplifier

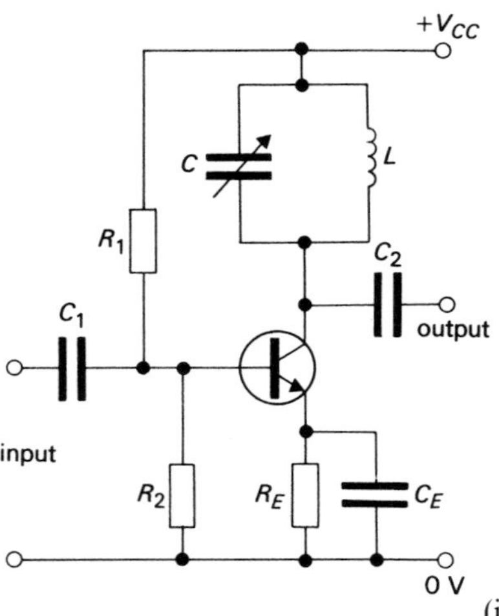

Figure 31 Typical circuit for a single stage radio frequency amplifier

The single stage audio amplifier (*class A*)

A typical circuit for a single stage transistor audio amplifier (class A) is illustrated in Figure 29. The potential divider chain R_1 and R_2 maintains a constant voltage between the base and zero potential, thus setting the quiescent point. Resistor R_E provides temperature compensation, and the shunt capacitor C_E decouples R_E from the output circuit at mid-band frequencies. Capacitor C_1 is a blocking capacitor, removing any unwanted d.c. from the input signal. Capacitor C_2 is also a blocking capacitor preventing any unwanted d.c. from appearing in the output or being passed to the next stage in multistage amplifiers. R_L is the collector load resistor. A detailed analysis of this single stage amplifier appears in topic area Small signal amplifiers in Electronics 2.

Figure 30 illustrates the frequency response of a typical audio amplifier. The values of the upper and lower cut-off frequencies, f_2 and f_1 respectively, are different for different applications of the audio amplifier. Typical values for the upper and lower cut-off frequencies and bandwidths are given in Figure 30 for various audio frequency amplifiers.

The single stage r.f. amplifier

The radio frequency (r.f.) amplifier differs from the audio amplifier in that only a narrow band of frequencies is amplified. Radio frequency amplifiers therefore employ a tuned circuit in order to select a narrow band of frequencies for amplification.

Figure 31 illustrates the circuit for a single stage radio frequency amplifier employing a capacitor C and inductor L as the tuned circuit, the resonant frequency of which is given by the formula

$$f_0 = \frac{1}{2\pi\sqrt{(LC)}} \quad \text{where } f_0 \text{ is the resonant frequency}$$

Frequency tuning of the tuned circuit is usually achieved by a variable capacitor, but is possible using a variable inductor. Varying the capacitance of C changes the resonant frequency of the tuned circuit, and therefore changes the mid-band frequency at which maximum gain occurs. Resistors R_1, R_2 and R_E and capacitor C_E perform the same function as in the audio amplifier of Figure 29. Capacitors C_1 and C_2 are blocking capacitors.

The tuned r.f. amplifier may perform several functions:

(i) amplify the r.f. signal

(ii) provide selectivity which is most important in reducing 'second channel' or image signals. This improves the pre-mixer selectivity

(iii) improve the signal to noise ratio for the system, and

(iv) protect the aerial in a receiver from receiving and radiating oscillations from the local oscillator stage, thus preventing interference to other receivers.

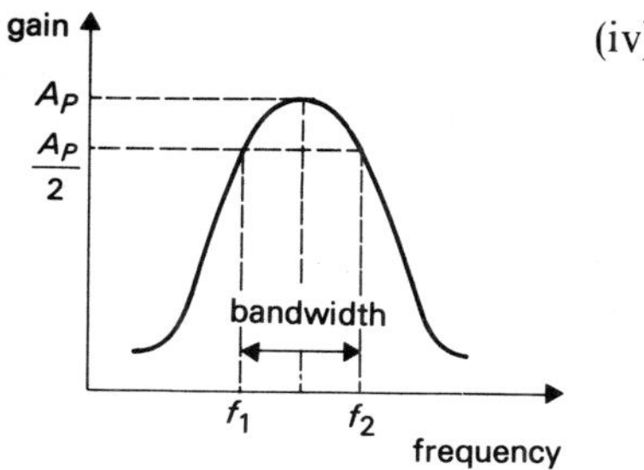

r.f. amplifier type	f_1 (MHz)	f_2 (MHz)	bandwidth (MHz)
f.m. receiver r.f. amplifier	87·75	90·25	2·5
u.h.f. television receiver r.f. amplifier	490	510	20

Figure 32 Frequency response of a single stage r.f. amplifier

Figure 32 illustrates the frequency response of a typical r.f. amplifier. These amplifiers are generally used in v.h.f./u.h.f. receivers for radio and television to improve the signal to noise ratio. They are rarely used in simple MW/LW receivers because the existing signal to noise ratio is adequate, except in communication and car radio receivers. They are also used in marine and aircraft communication receivers to stop the local oscillator from 'radiating' from the aerial. Typical values of the upper and lower cut-off frequencies and bandwidth for various r.f. amplifiers are given in Figure 32.

Selectivity

To select the correct signal a tuned amplifier needs as narrow a bandwidth as possible, i.e. the frequency response curve should be 'peaky'. Thus the narrower the bandwidth the more selective is the amplifier. Selectivity of an amplifier is the ability of the amplifier to separate signals whose frequencies are close together.

The single stage wideband amplifier

As their name suggests, wideband amplifiers are designed to amplify a wide range of frequencies. Wideband amplifiers sometimes need to amplify signals other than those with a sinusoidal shape, e.g. pulses in radar equipment, square waves in television systems and almost any waveform in oscilloscopes. Wideband amplifiers thus require a large bandwidth so as to amplify as many of the component frequencies of a signal as possible without distortion of the signal shape occurring.

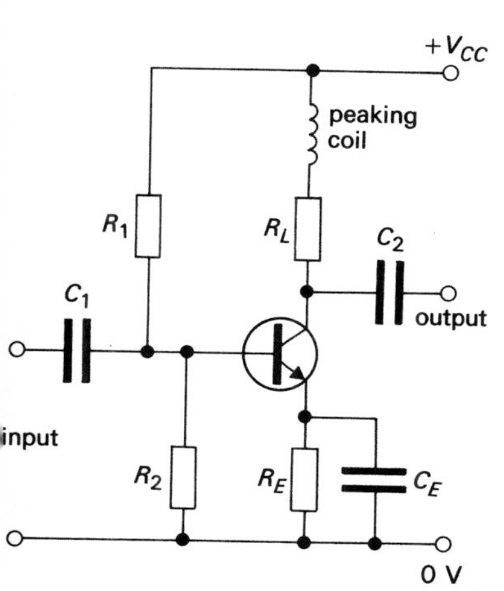

Figure 33 Typical circuit for a single stage wideband amplifier

Figure 33 illustrates a typical circuit for a single stage wideband amplifier. It is in fact similar to the audio amplifier of Figure 29 except that the collector load now consists of a series resistor R_L and a peaking coil. The purpose of the peaking coil is to extend the upper cut-off frequency thus increasing the bandwidth of the amplifier (see p. 29). The effect of the peaking coil is to give a lift in the output impedance at the high frequency end of the response curve, which tends to compensate for the decreasing reactance of the circuit stray capacitance. Stray capacitance is due to the siting of components and wiring of a circuit. A typical frequency response of a wideband amplifier is illustrated in Figure 34. Typical values of the upper and lower cut-off frequencies are also included for various wideband amplifiers.

The inclusion of the peaking coil often causes a 'hump' in th frequency response curve at the high frequency cut-off point. Thi causes no undesirable effect providing the fall-off rate is not too steep

[It is shown in topic area Feedback that the application of negativ feedback can also be used to extend the bandwidth.]

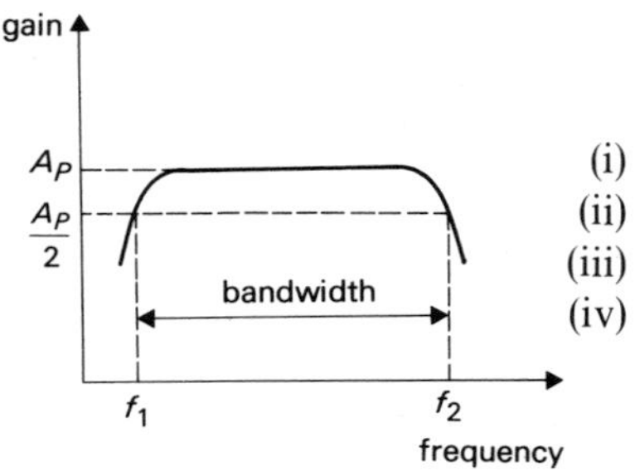

wideband amplifier type	f_1 (MHz)	f_2 (MHz)	bandwidth (MHz)
video amplifier for 625 line television system	35	41	6
oscilloscope	0 d.c.	3	3

Figure 34 Frequency response of a single stage wideband amplifier

The buffer amplifier

Amplifiers are often required to have all the following properties:

(i) a high input impedance
(ii) a low output impedance
(iii) no inversion between input and output signals
(iv) unity voltage gain.

Such amplifiers are often referred to as buffer amplifiers or feedbac amplifiers. Buffer amplifiers are used for matching a high to a lov impedance in amplifier stages in order to reduce loading an interaction between stages. They are utilized in series regulato circuits of stabilized power supplies, and often follow the maste oscillator stage in transmitters for isolation purposes and waveforn improvement.

Figure 35 illustrates a typical emitter follower circuit. The circui should be recognizable as the common collector mode of connectio for the bipolar transistor. Resistor R_1 is the base bias resistor and set the transistor quiescent base current and consequently the quiescen emitter current. The emitter resistor R_E limits the output voltage c the amplifier. Capacitors C_1 and C_2 are blocking capacitors for th input and output signals respectively.

[Further explanation of this circuit is considered in topic are Feedback.]

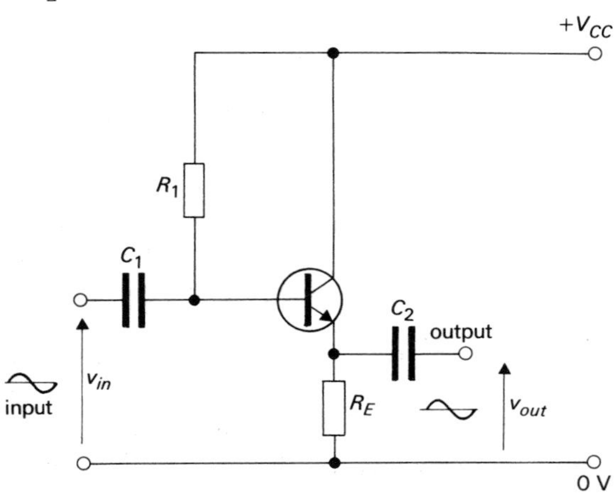

Figure 35 A typical emitter follower circuit

Self-assessment questions

Complete the following six questions by writing in the correct word. The questions all relate to small signal amplifiers except where otherwise stated.

1 The purpose of a small signal amplifier is to increase the__________ of the voltage of an electrical signal.

2 Large signal amplifiers are used to amplify the______________of an electrical signal.

3 The gain of an amplifier is the amount of increase of the output signal amplitude compared with the ______________ of the signal before amplification.

4 A graph of ______________ plotted against frequency gives a practical indication of the frequency response of the amplifier.

5 The graph which gives an indication of the amount of gain that may be obtained from an amplifying device is called the ______________ characteristic. The ______________ the slope of this graph the greater is the amplification of the device.

6 To obtain minimum amplitude distortion in practice, the mean level of the input signal is placed on the part of the curve that is most ______________. The positioning on the curve is achieved by what is known as ______________.

7 Write down two factors that determine the amount of amplification of an amplifier.

8 Explain the term frequency distortion.

9 Statement 1: In class A, the active device is biased at the midpoint on the linear part of the output characteristic.
Statement 2: In class B, current exists in the amplifier load only during one half cycle of the input signal.
(*a*) Only statement 1 is true
(*b*) Only statement 2 is true
(*c*) Both statements 1 and 2 are true
(*d*) Neither statement 1 nor 2 is true.
Underline the correct answer.

Complete Questions 10–15 by crossing out the incorrect option.

10 In class C, the active device is biased at the cut-off point.
TRUE/FALSE

11 The following list of classes of bias is in the correct order of ascending distortion:

class A
class B
class AB
class C

TRUE/FALSE

12 The following list of amplifiers is in the correct order of increasing bandwidths:

hi-fi audio amplifier
television r.f. amplifier
oscilloscope wideband amplifier

TRUE/FALSE

13 Wideband amplifiers amplify a large/small range of frequencies.

14 Wideband amplifiers amplify only sinusoidal signals.

TRUE/FALSE

15 The bandwidth of an audio amplifier is large/small compared to a wideband amplifier.

16 Match the following classes of bias labelled A, B, C to the applications labelled (i), (ii), (iii) and (iv) by placing the letter A, B, C next to the applications of each type. Each class of bias may be used once, more than once or not at all.

(i)	A.f. amplifiers	A	Class A
(ii)	R.f. amplifiers	B	Class B
(iii)	Oscillators	C	Class C
(iv)	Power supplies		

17 Statement 1: The r.f. amplifier has to amplify the r.f. signal.
Statement 2: The r.f. amplifier has to select the correct r.f. signal.

(*a*) Only statement 1 is true
(*b*) Only statement 2 is true
(*c*) Both statements 1 and 2 are true
(*d*) Neither statement 1 nor 2 is true.

Underline the correct answer.

18 Explain selectivity in a tuned amplifier.

19 List four properties of buffer amplifiers.

20 Statement 1: Buffer amplifiers are used for matching a high impedance to a low impedance.
Statement 2: Buffer amplifiers increase the loading and interaction between stages.

(*a*) Only statement 1 is true
(*b*) Only statement 2 is true
(*c*) Both statements 1 and 2 are true
(*d*) Neither statement 1 nor 2 is true.
Underline the correct answer.

21 Radio frequency amplifiers employ a tuned circuit, the resonant frequency of which is given by the equation:

$f_0 =$

Complete Questions 22–24 by selecting the correct alternative or inserting the missing word(s).

22 The purpose of a small signal amplifier is to increase the frequency of the voltage of an electrical signal.

TRUE/FALSE

23 In class AB, the bias point lies somewhere between the midpoint and the upper cut-off point on the output characteristics of the active device.

TRUE/FALSE

24 The frequency response of a hi-fi audio amplifier is typically ____________ Hz to ____________ Hz.

25 Sketch the frequency response of a typical r.f. amplifier utilized in television systems. Indicate typical values for the upper and lower cut-off frequencies.

26 What is the purpose of a peaking coil in a single stage wideband amplifier circuit?

27 Statement 1: In class AB, current exists for less than half a cycle of the input signal.
Statement 2: Class AB has a greater efficiency than class B but less distortion than class A.
(*a*) Only statement 1 is true
(*b*) Only statement 2 is true
(*c*) Both statements 1 and 2 are true
(*d*) Neither statement 1 nor 2 is true.
Underline the correct answer.

28 Given a typical circuit for a single stage transistor audio amplifier as shown in Figure 29, list the functions of the circuit components.

29 Given a typical circuit for a single stage transistor r.f. amplifier as shown in Figure 31, list the functions of the circuit components.

30 Given a typical circuit for a single stage transistor wideband amplifier as shown in Figure 33, list the functions of the circuit components.

After reading the following material, the reader shall:

3.7 Describe the following types of interstage coupling
(*a*) direct
(*b*) *R–C*
(*c*) transformer.

3.8 List the applications of the coupling methods stated in **3.7.**

3.9 State that for maximum efficiency impedance matching must be used in amplifier systems.

3.10 Describe the two stage
(*a*) direct coupled amplifier,
(*b*) differential amplifier,
(*c*) *R–C* coupled common emitter amplifier.

3.11 Predict the performance of a two stage class A common emitter amplifier.

3.12 Measure the frequency response of the circuit **3.10**(*c*).

3.13 Measure signal amplitude limits for operation of the amplifier of **3.10**(*c*).

3.14 Measure the effect on the stage gain and bandwidth of disconnecting the emitter bypass capacitor.

3.15 Measure the input and output impedance of the two stage amplifier in **3.10**(*c*).

In earlier sections of this chapter single stage a.c. amplifiers have been considered. Very often, a gain is required which is very much greater than that of a single stage. Consequently several single stages need to be joined together (cascaded) in order to increase the overall gain of the amplifiers. Amplifiers require a d.c. supply in order to amplify the a.c. signal. Hence, in cascaded a.c. amplifiers the individual stages must be joined together in such a way that only the a.c. signal is passed on to the next stage, the d.c. operating conditions being blocked. The common methods employed to couple a.c. amplifier stages include *resistance–capacitance* and *transformer coupling* which is generally of low impedance to prevent attenuation of the signal being amplified.

In d.c. amplifiers however the d.c. signal must be transferred between successive stages. Amplifiers designed to amplify low frequency signals (d.c. amplifiers) use *direct coupling* between stages; i.e. there are no reactive components in the coupling circuit.

Audio and wideband amplifiers tend to employ an *R–C network* as the coupling circuit; the capacitor blocks the d.c. but allows the a.c. signal to pass to the next stage for further amplification. *Transformer coupling* is used in audio power amplifiers and radio frequency amplifiers. Coupling via a transformer has two advantages:

(i) it ensures isolation between amplifier stages, since the primary and secondary windings of the transformer are electrically isolated
(ii) it allows for maximum transfer of power since the source and load impedances can be matched, i.e. made equal.

Solutions to self-assessment questions (pages 45–48)

1 Amplitude.

2 Power.

3 Amplitude.

4 Gain.

5 Transfer, steeper.

6 Linear, biasing.

7
(i) The number of amplifier stages used, or
(ii) The design of the amplifier stage, or
(iii) The characteristics of the device used in the amplifier stage.

8 An input signal to an amplifier that contains frequencies outside the passband of the amplifier cannot be reproduced exactly at the output of the amplifier because signals outside the passband are amplified at values different from those inside the passband. This causes distortion of the output signal known as frequency distortion.

9 (*c*) Both statements are true.

10 FALSE. In class C the active device is biased beyond cut-off.

11 FALSE. The list should be
class A
class AB
class B
class C

12 FALSE. The list should be:
television r.f. amplifier
hi-fi audio amplifier
oscilloscope wideband amplifier

13 Wideband amplifiers amplify a *large* range of frequencies.

14 FALSE. Wideband amplifiers amplify sinusoidal signals, pulses and square waves.

15 The bandwidth of an audio amplifier is *small* compared to a wideband amplifier.

16
(i) A.f. amplifiers A, B
(ii) R.f. amplifiers B, C
(iii) Oscillators C
(iv) Power supplies None

17 (*c*) Both statements are true.

18 Selectivity of a tuned amplifier is the ability of the amplifier to separate signals whose frequencies are close together. This may be achieved by using as narrow a bandwidth as possible.

19
(i) High input impedance
(ii) Low output impedance
(iii) Unity voltage gain
(iv) No signal inversion between input and output.

20 (*a*) Statement 2 should read: Buffer amplifiers reduce the loading and interaction between stages.

21 $f_0 = \dfrac{1}{2\pi\sqrt{(LC)}}$

22 FALSE. The purpose of a small signal amplifier is to increase the magnitude of the voltage of an electrical signal.

23 TRUE.

24 30 Hz to 30 kHz

25 See Figure 32.

26 The purpose of the peaking coil in a wideband amplifier is to extend the upper cut-off frequency and thus increase the amplifier bandwidth.

27 (*d*) Statement 1 should read: In class AB current exists for more than one half cycle, but less than the complete cycle of the input signal.
Statement 2 should read: Class AB has a greater efficiency than class A but less distortion than class B.

28 With reference to Figure 29:
R_1 and R_2 maintain a constant voltage between base and zero potential.
R_E provides temperature compensation.
C_E decouples R_E from the output circuit at mid-band frequencies.
C_1 and C_2 are blocking capacitors which remove unwanted d.c. from the signal.
R_1 is the collector load resistor.

29 With reference to Figure 31:
R_1 and R_2 maintain a constant voltage between base and zero potential.
R_E provides temperature compensation.
C_E decouples R_E from the output circuit at mid-band frequencies.
C_1 and C_2 are blocking capacitors which remove unwanted d.c. from the signal.
C and L form the tuned circuit to achieve frequency tuning.

30 With reference to Figure 33:
R_L and peaking coil are the collector load with the peaking coil extending the upper cut-off frequency.
R_1 and R_2 maintain a constant voltage between base and zero potential.
R_E provides temperature compensation.
C_E decouples R_E from the output circuit at mid-band frequencies.
C_1 and C_2 are blocking capacitors which remove unwanted d.c. from the signal.

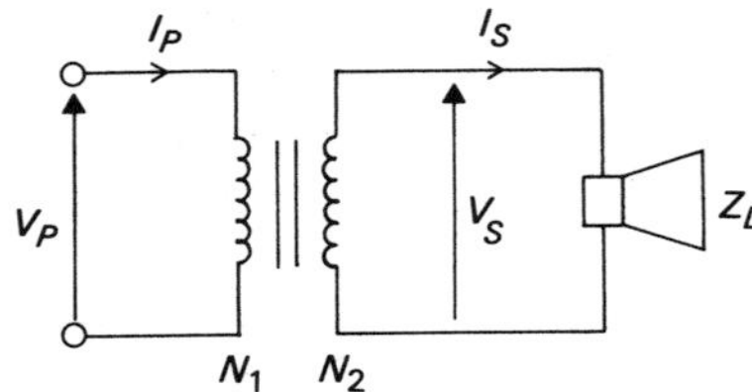

Figure 36 Circuit to illustrate maximum power transfer

Consider the circuit of Figure 36.

Let Z_{in} = input impedance of the signal source

$$Z_{in}=\frac{V_p}{I_p} \text{ and } Z_L=\frac{V_s}{I_s}$$

Assuming an ideal transformer, $\dfrac{V_p}{V_s}=\dfrac{N_1}{N_2}=\dfrac{I_s}{I_p}$

$$\therefore Z_{in}=\frac{V_s\times\dfrac{N_1}{N_2}}{I_s\times\dfrac{N_2}{N_1}}$$

$$=\frac{V_s}{I_s}\left(\frac{N_1}{N_2}\right)^2$$

$$\therefore Z_{in}=Z_L\left(\frac{N_1}{N_2}\right)^2 \text{ since } \frac{V_s}{I_s}=Z_L$$

The transformer may thus be regarded as a device which transforms impedance by the square of the turns ratio of the transformer. Transformer coupling is thus very useful in audio power amplifiers, where it is desirable to transfer maximum signal power to the speaker.

The direct coupled amplifier

The direct coupled amplifier amplifies all frequencies from zero frequency to the upper cut-off frequency (f_2). A typical frequency response of a direct coupled amplifier is shown in Figure 37. In order to amplify low frequency signals, direct coupled amplifiers must have no reactive components in their coupling networks.

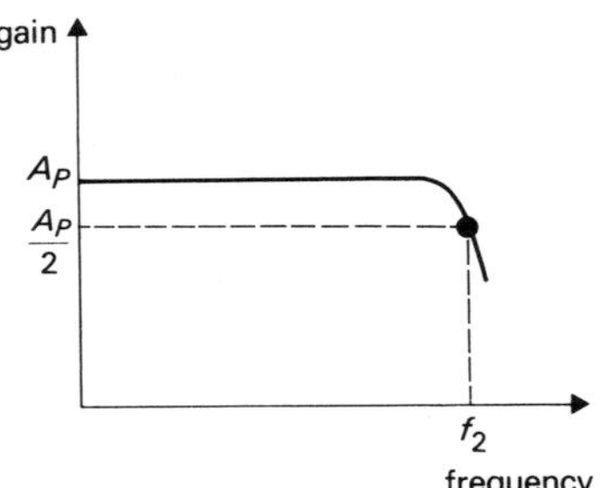

Figure 37 Frequency response of a direct coupled amplifier

Figure 38 illustrates the circuit of a two stage direct coupled amplifier. The two transistors are directly coupled, the collector of transistor T1 being at the same potential as the base of transistor T2. This involves careful design in order to ensure the correct circuit potentials. Any changes in voltage levels in the first stage due to temperature change or supply voltage variations are amplified by the second stage, which itself is affected by external changes. The change in voltage levels is known as *drift*, which is difficult to distinguish from low frequency signals. To reduce the problem of drift, consider the circuit of Figure 39 which shows two separate common emitter amplifiers with their emitters coupled together. The circuit is commonly called a *differential amplifier* – the output signal being the *difference* between the two collector values. If two identical signals are applied to input 1 and input 2, the output is zero because both collector values change by the same amount (providing both transistors are matched). This is known as the *common mode* operation. If two similar signals, but of opposite polarity, are applied to input 1 and input 2, the amplitude of the output signal is twice that obtainable from one transistor, since the currents through each transistor change by the same magnitude, but the directions of the currents are opposite to each other. This is known as the *differential mode* operation. The circuit of Figure 39 is thus immune to drift because any changes which occur, affect each transistor equally. It is for this reason that the differential amplifier finds its greatest use in integrated circuits (see topic area Integrated circuits).

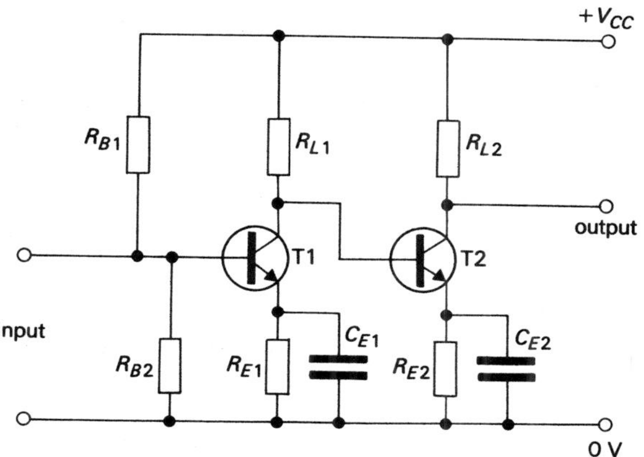

Figure 38 Typical circuit for a two stage direct coupled amplifier

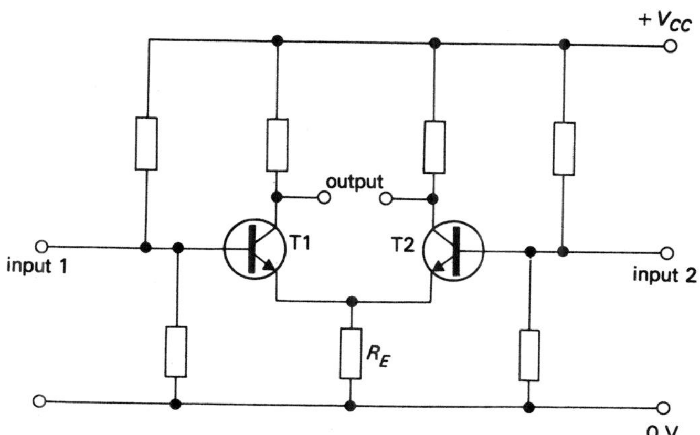

Figure 39 Typical differential amplifier

The R–C coupled amplifier

Figure 40 illustrates the circuit diagram of a two stage *R–C* coupled common emitter amplifier. Resistors R_1, R_2 and R_5, R_6 are the d.c. bias resistors for each stage. R_4 and R_8 are the circuit stabilization components. Capacitors C_3 and C_4 are the emitter bypass capacitors for the decoupling of resistors R_4 and R_8 respectively. R_3 and R_7 are the collector load resistors of the transistors T1 and T2 respectively. C_2 is the coupling capacitor for the two stages. C_1 and C_5 are blocking capacitors for the input and output respectively.

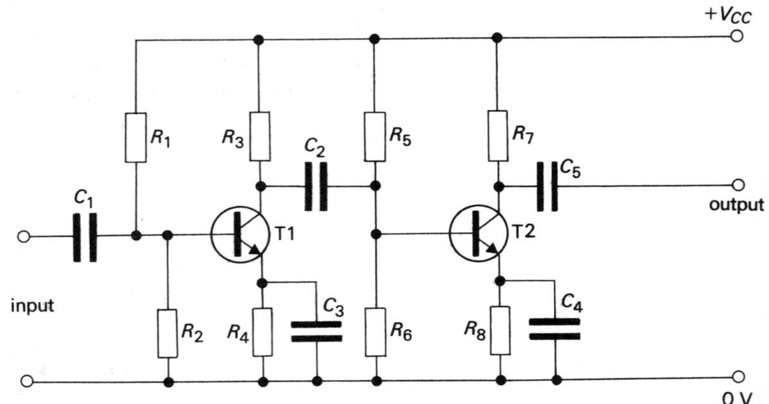

Figure 40 Typical two stage R–C coupled common emitter amplifier

Example 1

Figure 41 illustrates a typical circuit diagram of an R–C coupled two stage amplifier with component values which use two BC108 transistors, having the following parameters:

an input impedance of 4 kΩ

and current gain h_{fe} of 150

Predict the gain of

(i) each stage

(ii) the amplifier

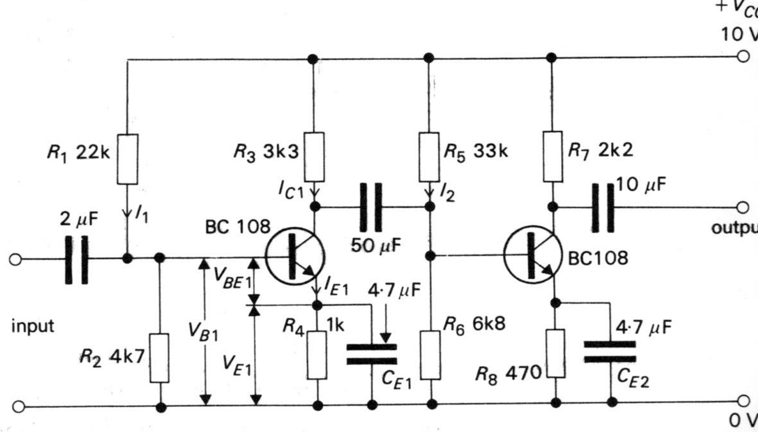

Figure 41 Typical circuit diagram of an R–C coupled two stage amplifier (with component values)

Consider the first stage:

$$I_1 = \frac{V_{CC}}{R_1 + R_2}$$

$$I_1 = \frac{10}{26{\cdot}7 \times 10^{-3}}\ \text{mA} = 0{\cdot}37\ \text{mA}$$

$$V_{B1} = I_1 \times R_2 \qquad = 0{\cdot}37 \times 10^{-3} \times 4{\cdot}7 \times 10^3\ \text{V}$$

$$= 1{\cdot}73\ \text{V} \quad (I_B \text{ is negligible})$$

$$V_{E1} = 1{\cdot}73 - V_{BE} \qquad = (1{\cdot}73 - 0{\cdot}6)\ \text{V} \quad (V_{BE} = 0{\cdot}6\ \text{V for silicon transistors})$$

$$= 1{\cdot}13\ \text{V}$$

$$I_{E1} = \frac{1{\cdot}13}{1 \times 10^3} \qquad = 1{\cdot}13\ \text{mA}$$

Now $I_{E1} \approx I_{C1}$ (since I_B is small – usually measured in microamperes)

$$V_{C1} = V_{CC} - V_{R3}$$

$$= 10 - (1{\cdot}13 \times 10^{-3} \times 3{\cdot}3 \times 10^3)\ \text{V}$$

$$= 6{\cdot}27\ \text{V}$$

Voltage gain of first stage $A_{v1} = \dfrac{V_{out}}{V_{in}} = \dfrac{I_{out}R_{out}}{I_{in}R_{in}}$

$$= \frac{R_{out}}{R_{in}} \times h_{fe}$$

But R_{out} is 3·3 kΩ in parallel with 33 kΩ in parallel with 6·8 kΩ in parallel with input resistance of transistor 2, i.e.

$$\frac{1}{R_{out}} = \frac{1}{3{\cdot}3\ k\Omega} + \frac{1}{33\ k\Omega} + \frac{1}{6{\cdot}8\ k\Omega} + \frac{1}{4\ k\Omega}$$

$$R_{out} = 1{\cdot}37\ k\Omega$$

$$\therefore\ A_{v1} = \frac{1{\cdot}37 \times 10^3}{4 \times 10^3} \times 150 = 50{\cdot}30$$

Consider the second stage:

$$I_2 = \frac{10}{(33 + 6{\cdot}8)10^3}\ \text{A} = 0{\cdot}25\ \text{mA}$$

$$V_{B2} = 0{\cdot}25 \times 10^{-3} \times 6{\cdot}8 \times 10^3\ \text{V} = 1{\cdot}7\ \text{V}$$

$$V_{E2} = (1{\cdot}7 - 0{\cdot}6)\ \text{V} = 1{\cdot}1\ \text{V}$$

$$I_{E2} = \frac{V_{E2}}{R_8} = \frac{1{\cdot}1}{470}\ \text{A} = 2{\cdot}3\ \text{mA}$$

$$I_{C2} \approx I_{E2}$$

$$\therefore\ V_{C2} = 10 - (2{\cdot}34 \times 10^{-3} \times 2{\cdot}2 \times 10^{3})\ \text{V} = 4{\cdot}85\ \text{V}$$

Voltage gain of second stage, $A_{v2} = \dfrac{R_{out}}{R_{in}} \times h_{fe}$

$$= \frac{2{\cdot}2 \times 10^{3}}{4 \times 10^{3}} \times 150$$

$$A_{v2} = 82.5$$

Amplifier gain, $A_v = A_{v1} \times A_{v2}$

$$= 50{\cdot}3 \times 82{\cdot}5$$

$$A_v = 4150$$

The reader may wish to build the circuit of Figure 41 and use it to measure:

(i) the frequency response
(ii) the signal amplitude limits
(iii) the effect on the stage gain and bandwidth of disconnecting the emitter bypass capacitor, and
(iv) the input and output impedance.

(i) Measuring the frequency response

This is achieved by connecting a variable frequency sinusoidal signal having constant amplitude (say 1 mV) to the input of the circuit of Figure 41. An oscilloscope is connected across the output terminals so that the amplitude of the output signal may be measured. The frequency of the input signal is varied, say, from zero to 100 kHz. The amplitude of the output signal is measured on the oscilloscope at each frequency increment. The frequency response of the amplifier can now be plotted and will have the general shape as shown in Figure 24. The bandwidth may be measured from the frequency response curve.

(ii) Measuring the signal amplitude limits

With the input signal frequency constant, say at 1 kHz, the amplitude of the input signal is increased until distortion of the output signal occurs. This will be seen on the oscilloscope which is connected across the output terminals. Measurement of the amplitude of the input signal when distortion occurs is the signal amplitude limit for the amplifier.

(iii) Measuring the effect of the emitter bypass capacitor

The procedure outlined in (*i*) above may be repeated for the circuit of Figure 41 with

(*a*) C_{E1} only disconnected and
(*b*) C_{E2} only disconnected.

The effect of disconnecting the two capacitors may be observed by plotting the frequency response curve for each disconnection.

(iv) Measuring the input and output impedance

Impedance contains both resistance and reactance and since reactance varies with frequency so does impedance. It is common practice to measure the input and output impedance of an amplifier at some fixed frequency, usually 1 kHz.

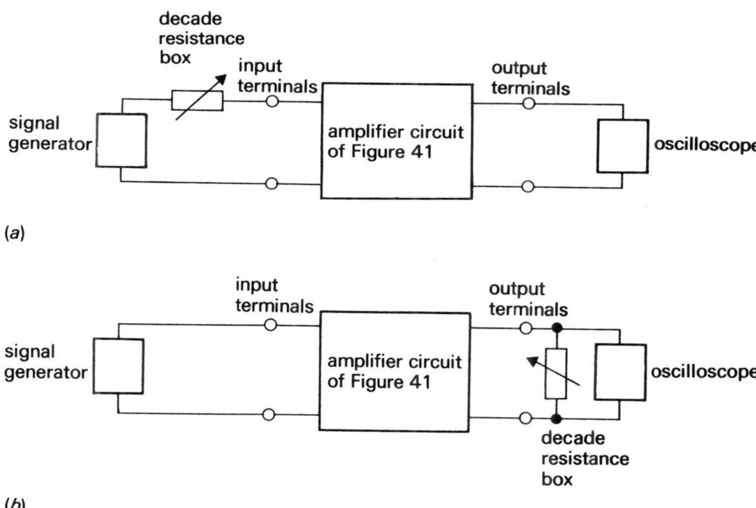

Figure 42 Circuit for determining the input and output impedance of an amplifier

(a) measurement of input impedance
(b) measurement of output impedance

As shown in Figure 42(*a*), a signal generator in series with a decade resistance box is connected to the input terminals of the amplifier circuit of Figure 41. An oscilloscope is connected across the output terminals. The decade resistance box is set to zero and a 1 kHz constant amplitude sinusoidal input signal is applied to the amplifier. The amplitude of the output signal is measured on the oscilloscope. The resistance of the decade box is now increased until the magnitude of the output signal is reduced to half the original value. The ohmic value of the decade resistance box is then equal to the inpu impedance of the amplifier. The decade resistance box and th amplifier are behaving as a potential divider network and when thei ohmic values are equal, the potential across each is the same, i.e. whe the output voltage is equal to half the input voltage.

The output impedance is measured in a similar way except this tim the decade resistance box is connected across the output terminals a shown in Figure 42(*b*).

Self-assessment questions

31 Describe three methods by which amplifier stages may be cascaded

32 The output stage in a radio receiver has an optimum load impedanc of 1 kΩ. Calculate the turns ratio of a matching transformer to suppl a loudspeaker of 8 Ω so that maximum power is delivered to th loudspeaker.

Complete Questions 33–35 by writing in the correct word(s).

33 A direct coupled amplifier amplifies all frequencies fror __________ to the __________.

34 Drift, which occurs in direct coupled amplifiers, is caused by th change in voltage levels in the first stage due to__________ change or __________ variations being amplified by th second stage.

35 A differential amplifier can be operated either in the__________ mode or the __________ mode.

Questions 36–39 relate to the circuit diagram of Figure 43. Assumin that the transistors are matched, complete the questions by insertin the missing word(s).

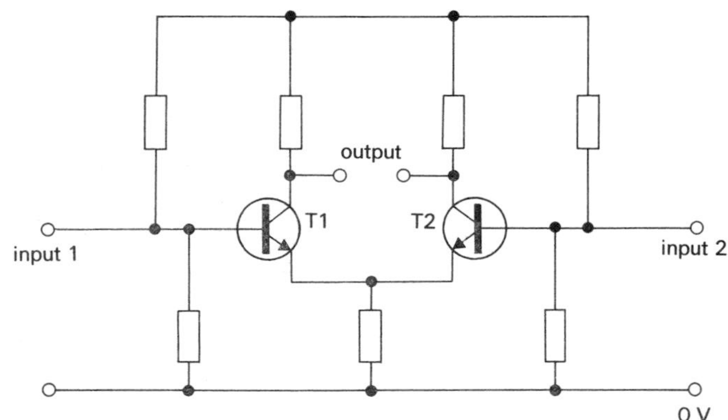

Figure 43 circuit diagram for Self-assessment questions 36–39

36 When two identical signals are applied to input 1 and input 2 the measured change in output is ____________

37 The form of operation in Question 36 is known as the ____________ mode.

38 If two identical signals, but of opposite polarity, are applied to input 1 and input 2, the measured change in the output is ____________ that obtainable from one transistor.

39 The form of operation in Question 38 is known as the ____________ mode.

40 Match the list of coupling circuits labelled A, B, C to the amplifier systems labelled (i), (ii), (iii), (iv) which use them by placing the letters A, B, C next to the amplifier systems. Each letter may be used once, more than once or not at all.

(i)	audio amplifiers	A	direct coupled
(ii)	d.c. amplifiers	B	*R–C* coupled
(iii)	r.f. amplifiers	C	transformer coupled
(iv)	wideband amplifiers		

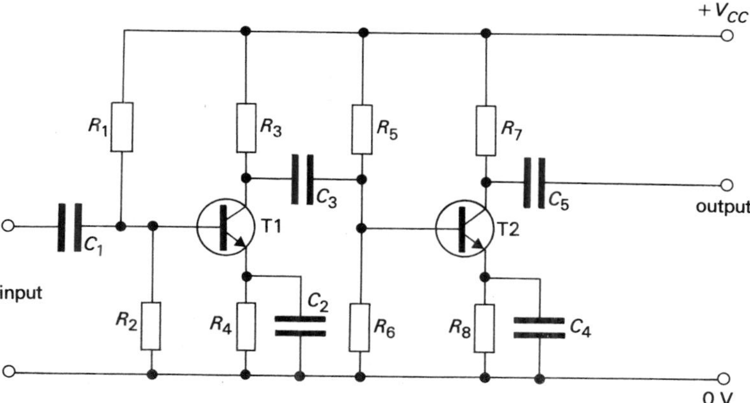

Figure 44 Circuit diagram for Self-assessment question 41

41 Figure 44 illustrates the circuit diagram of a two stage *R–C* coupled common emitter amplifier.
Match the functions listed A, B, C,... to the circuit components labelled (1), (2), (3),... by placing the letters A, B, C,... next to the circuit components. Each letter may be used once, more than once or not at all.

(1) R_1	A temperature stabilization
(2) R_2	B biasing
(3) R_3	C decoupling
(4) R_4	D coupling

(5) R_5 E charging
(6) R_6 F amplification
(7) R_7 G loading
(8) R_8
(9) C_1
(10) C_2
(11) C_3
(12) C_4
(13) C_5
(14) T1
(15) T2

42 State why impedance matching must be used in amplifier systems.

43 List the procedure for measuring the frequency response of an *R-C* coupled two stage amplifier.

After reading the following material, the reader shall:

4 Describe the action of large signal amplifiers.
4.1 Explain that in amplifier systems four types of distortion are possible
(i) harmonic or amplitude
(ii) frequency
(iii) phase
(iv) intermodulation.
4.2 State the methods employed to reduce distortion.
4.3 Identify from given circuit diagrams the following a.f. large signal amplifiers
(*a*) single-ended
(*b*) push-pull
(*c*) complementary.
4.4 List the functions of individual components in the large signal amplifier circuits of **4.3.**
4.5 State the reasons for and the effects of parasitic oscillations in large signal amplifiers.
4.6 State the methods of suppressing parasitic oscillations.

Distortion

It has been seen that when an amplifier is operating in the class A mode, the output signal is theoretically a faithful replica of the input signal. In practice, this may not be true if the transfer characteristic is not linear; in this case *distortion* of the signal occurs. Distortion may occur in several different forms.

(*i*) *Harmonic or amplitude distortion*

This occurs in amplifier systems when the input signal is so large that the active device of the amplifier does not operate within the linear range of its characteristics. Figure 45(*a*) illustrates the distortion produced when a transistor is operated outside its linear characteristics. The output is distorted and contains frequencies (known as harmonics) which are not present in the input signal. The amount of distortion is dependent upon the magnitude of the input signal. Harmonic or amplitude distortion can be reduced in small signal amplifiers by operating in class A with a small magnitude input signal. In large signal amplifiers, the amplifier can be connected in a push-pull arrangement (see pages 61 to 63).

(*ii*) *Frequency distortion*

This occurs in amplifier systems when the input signal is a complex wave consisting of harmonics which are not amplified equally. It affects frequencies which lie above the upper cut-off frequency and below the lower cut-off frequency of the amplifier. An amplifier with a frequency response shown in Figure 45(*b*) amplifies the frequencies more in the mid-band range than those outside the mid-band range. Frequency distortion can be reduced by increasing the bandwidth of the amplifier, i.e. by choosing the capacitive elements in the amplifier carefully so that the upper cut-off frequency increases and the lower cut-off frequency decreases. Also negative feedback can be applied to the amplifier to increase the bandwidth.

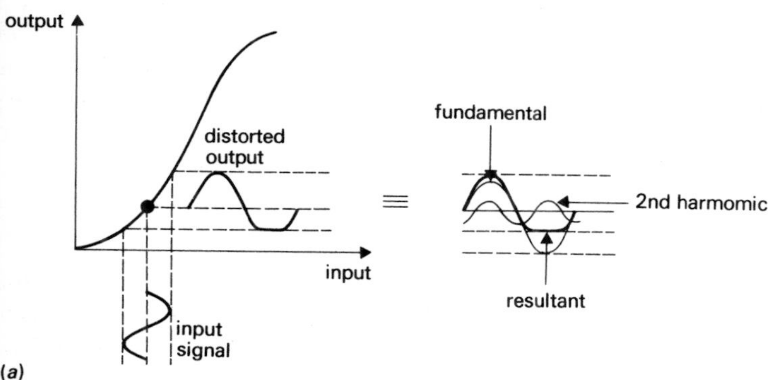

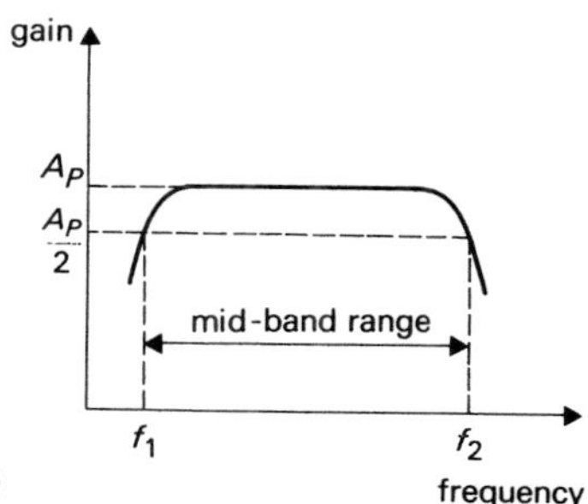

Figure 45 Types of distortion
(a) harmonic or amplitude distortion
(b) frequency distortion

Solutions to self-assessment questions (pages 56–58)

31 Amplifier stages may be:

(i) direct coupled where there are no reactive components in the coupling circuit

(ii) R–C coupled where the capacitor blocks the d.c. operating conditions but allows the a.c. signal to pass to the next stage

(iii) transformer coupled which ensures isolation between amplifier stages and also provides matching between previous stage and next stage or load.

32 $$\frac{Z_{in}}{Z_L}=\left(\frac{N_1}{N_2}\right)^2$$

$$\frac{N_1}{N_2}=\left(\frac{Z_{in}}{Z_L}\right)^{\frac{1}{2}}$$

$$=\left(\frac{1000}{8}\right)^{\frac{1}{2}}$$

$$=(125)^{\frac{1}{2}}$$

$$\approx 11$$

∴ Turns ratio is 11:1

33 Zero, the upper cut-off frequency.

34 Temperature change, supply voltage.

35 Common, differential.

36 Zero.

37 Common.

38 Twice.

39 Differential.

40

(i)	audio amplifiers	B, C
(ii)	d.c. amplifiers	A
(iii)	r.f. amplifiers	C
(iv)	wideband amplifiers	B

41

(1) R_1	B
(2) R_2	B
(3) R_3	D, G
(4) R_4	A
(5) R_5	B
(6) R_6	B
(7) R_7	G
(8) R_8	A
(9) C_1	C
(10) C_2	C
(11) C_3	D
(12) C_4	C
(13) C_5	C
(14) $T1$	F
(15) $T2$	F

42 Impedance matching must be use[d] in amplifier systems so that maxi[mum] signal power may be tran[s]ferred between stages. This is part[i]cularly useful in audio power am[]plifiers to transfer maximum sign[al] power to the speaker.

43

(i) Connect a variable frequency sin[u]soidal signal having a consta[nt] amplitude to the input of th[e] amplifier

(ii) Connect an oscilloscope across th[e] output terminals

(iii) Vary the frequency of the inp[ut] signal

(iv) Measure the amplitude of the ou[t]put signal at each frequenc[y] increment

(v) Plot the frequency response of th[e] amplifier.

(iii) Phase distortion

Any non-sinusoidal waveshape can be considered to be a comple[x] wave with component frequencies. If each of these is not delayed by a[n] equal time interval (from input to output), then the output wavefor[m] is not an exact replica of the input, and phase distortion (or dela[y] distortion) occurs. Thus, phase distortion occurs when there is [a] phase shift between the input and output signal. Phase distortion is o[f] no real consequence in audio amplifiers since it does not affect th[e] amplifier volume, but it is important in television video amplifier[s] because picture quality is affected. Phase distortion may be reduce[d] by the application of negative feedback to the amplifier.

(iv) Intermodulation distortion

This occurs in amplifier systems due to the nonlinear characteristic of the active device when amplifying complex waveforms. It results i[n] frequencies in the output waveform which bear no harmoni[c] relationship to the input waveform, i.e. the output contains the su[m] and difference of frequencies of the input. Intermodulation distortio[n] can be reduced by applying the same methods as for harmoni[c] distortion.

Single ended amplifier

Figure 46 illustrates a typical circuit diagram for a *single ended* a.f. power amplifier operating in class A. It is termed single ended because only *one* transistor is employed. The emitter resistor R_E provides thermal stability, its value being typically about 0·5 Ω. Resistor R_1 sets the required quiescent base current. Any variation in the base–emitter voltage affects the quiescent point. Consequently a thermistor R_2 is employed to compensate for any changes in the base emitter voltage. Transformer TR1 is employed for impedance matching purposes. Theoretically single ended class A a.f. power amplifiers cannot have an efficiency greater than 50 per cent, although in practice 30 per cent efficiency is considered to be excellent. Single ended class A amplifiers also suffer from power being wasted in the collector.

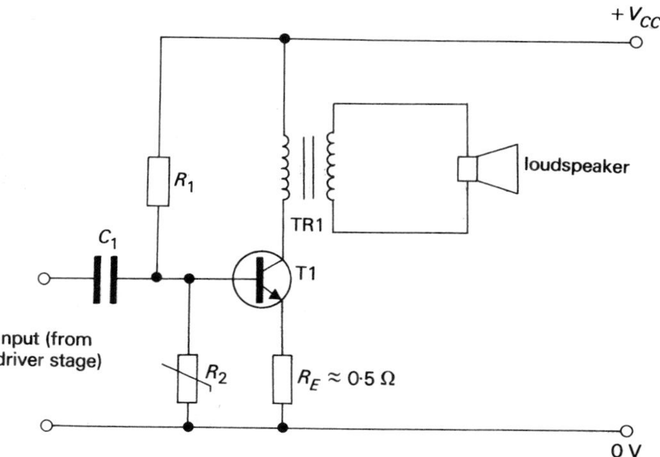

Figure 46 Typical circuit diagram for a single-ended class A a.f. power amplifier

Push-pull amplifiers

When more power is required than that of the single ended amplifier, two transistors are employed in a push-pull arrangement, as shown in Figure 47. Resistors R_1 and R_2 provide the necessary quiescent base current for transistors T1 and T2 respectively. Transformer TR2 is centre tapped; current flows in opposite directions in each half of the transformer primary winding to the collector of each transistor. The net effect of the currents flowing in each half of the transformer primary winding is to reduce the distortion. Transformer TR1 is also centre tapped and acts as a phase splitter. When the base of T1 increases positively, the base of T2 increases negatively by the same amount; when the base of T2 increases negatively, the base of T1 increases positively by the same amount. The output power of the push-pull circuit is thus twice that of the single ended amplifier. Less distortion occurs because all the even harmonics are cancelled by th push-pull arrangement (providing the transistors are matched). smaller output transformer (TR2) is required because current flowin in opposite directions in each half of the primary winding produce zero magnetization. Power supply ripple and noise are also elin inated in a push-pull arrangement.

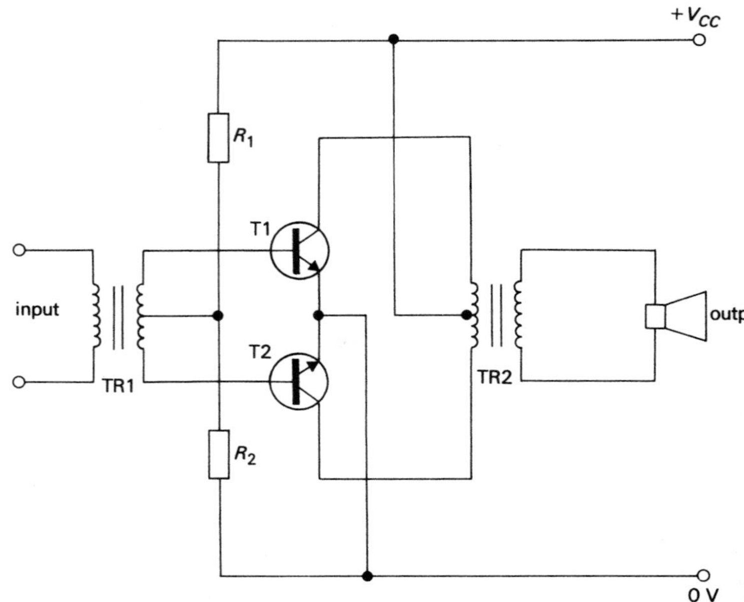

Figure 47 Push-pull class A a.f. power amplifier

The great disadvantage of class A amplifiers is their poor efficienc and class B is therefore employed to increase the efficiency. Figure 4 illustrates a typical class B push-pull a.f. power amplifier. Resistors and R_2 provide the quiescent base current of transistors T1 and T which once again should be matched. Resistor R_3 provides th required thermal stability. In class B, both T1 and T2 are biased cut-off. When the input signal increases positively the base of T increases positively, T2 being biased now beyond cut-off. When th input signal increases negatively the base of T2 increases negativel T1 being biased now beyond cut-off. Push-pull action thus occurs an each transistor conducts on alternate half cycles of the input signa each half cycle being reproduced in the primary coil of transform TR2. Class B amplifiers have a greater efficiency than class amplifiers – theoretically their efficiency is 78 per cent. With class operation the collector current is zero on 'no signal'. This is usef with battery operated equipment such as hearing aids and car radio

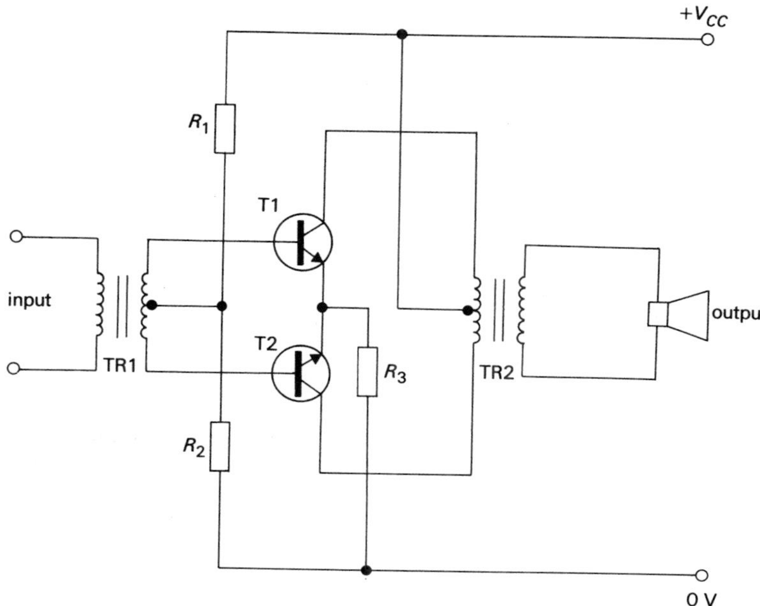

Figure 48 Push-pull class B a.f. power amplifier

Complementary push-pull amplifiers

Both n-p-n and p-n-p bipolar transistors are manufactured, each relying on supplies of opposite polarity for their operation. Push-pull circuits may be designed therefore without the use of transformers. Figure 49 illustrates such a circuit, which is commonly referred to as a complementary push-pull circuit. Once again both transistors should be matched, i.e. have similar transfer characteristics. T1 is an n-p-n transistor and T2 a p-n-p transistor. Resistors R_1 and R_2 apply slight forward bias to the base of each transistor. This ensures that collector current flows through each transistor at all times, and that crossover distortion is prevented. When the input signal increases positively, the current through T1 increases, T2 being cut-off. When the input signal increases negatively, the current through T2 increases, T1 being cut-off. The output signal is the sum of the two half cycles of each transistor during their push-pull action.

Parasitic oscillations in amplifier systems

Oscillations occur in amplifier systems due to the self capacitance and inductance of the circuit components, e.g. the leads of a resistor, the electrodes of a transistor or valve. The reactances of these components may sometimes set up series/parallel networks which can

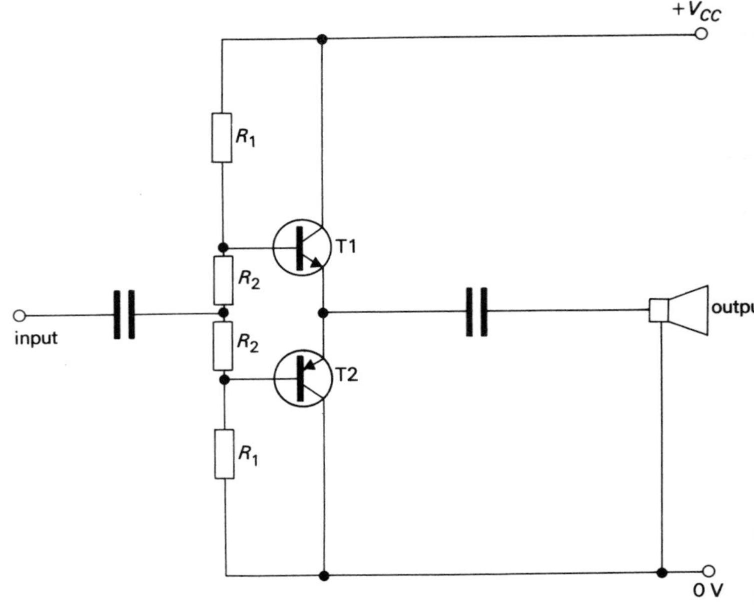

Figure 49 Complementing push-pull circuit

ruin the quiescent conditions of the active devices and caus harmonic distortion to occur. The reactances may also act as a tune circuit and produce self oscillations. These are often referred to a parasitic oscillations and invariably produce unpleasant sounds i the output stages of audio amplifiers.

Parasitic oscillations in audio power amplifiers can be reduced b using short, closely spaced component leads – effectively reducin the self capacitance and inductance of circuit components. Suppl lines can be decoupled by shunting them with a capacitor of larg capacitance and inserting a resistor in series with the supply effectively increasing the impedance.

Self-assessment questions

44 Explain how harmonic distortion occurs.

45 How can harmonic distortion be minimized in small and large sign amplifiers?

46 List three types of distortion which may occur in amplifier systems. Do not include the type given in Questions **44** and **45**.

47 Statement 1: A single ended power amplifier utilizes one transistor.
Statement 2: The theoretical efficiency of class A power amplifiers is 78 per cent.
(*a*) Only statement 1 is true
(*b*) Only statement 2 is true
(*c*) Both statements 1 and 2 are true
(*d*) Neither statement 1 nor 2 is true.
Underline the correct answer.

48 Figure 50 illustrates circuit diagrams of three transistor power amplifiers labelled (a), (b) and (c). Identify each type.

49 Statement 1: The theoretical efficiency of class B power amplifiers is 78 per cent.
Statement 2: Class B power amplifiers are utilized in battery operated equipment because the collector current is always zero.
(*a*) Only statement 1 is true
(*b*) Only statement 2 is true
(*c*) Both statements 1 and 2 are true
(*d*) Neither statement 1 nor 2 is true.
Underline the correct answer.

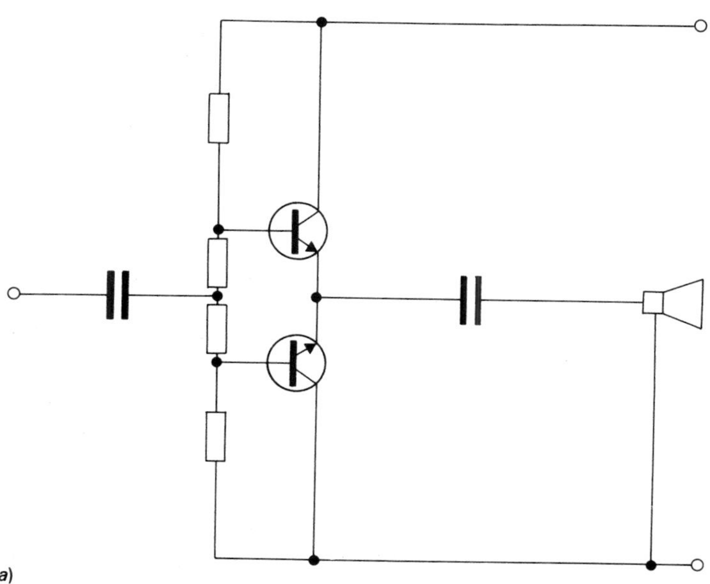

Figure 50 Circuit diagram for Self-assessment question 48

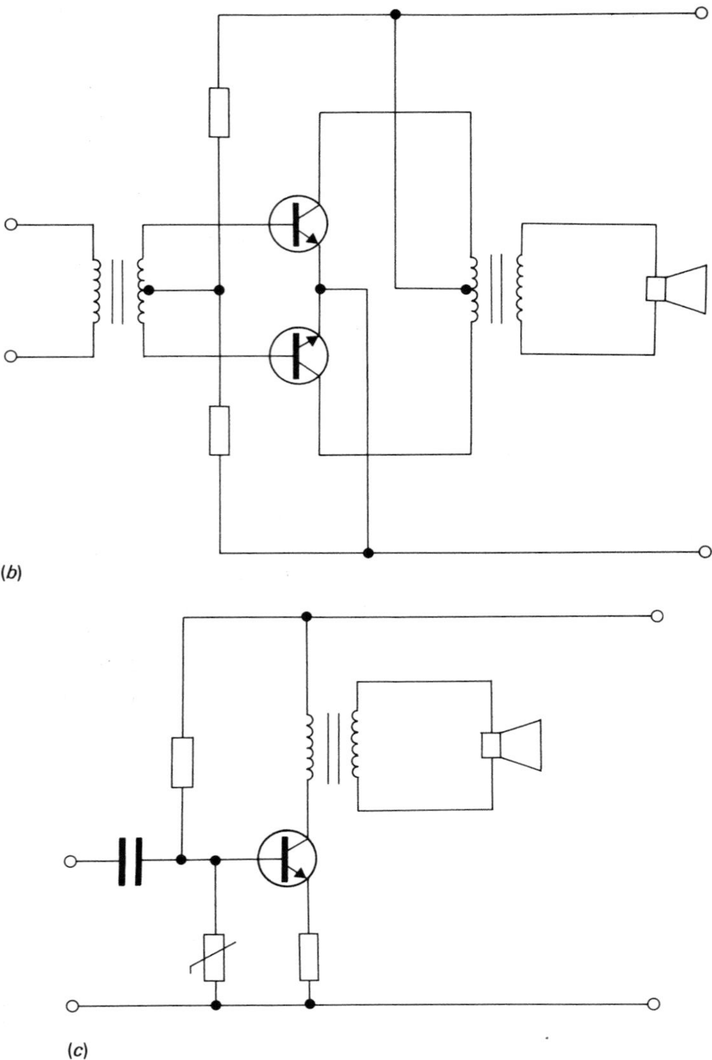

Figure 50 Circuit diagram for Self-assessment question 48

In Questions 50–53 cross out the incorrect option(s) or insert the missing word(s).

50 The output power of a push-pull amplifier circuit is twice that of a single ended amplifier circuit, provided that the transistors are matched.

TRUE/FALSE

51 Less distortion occurs in push-pull amplifier circuits than single-ended amplifier circuits because all even harmonics are cancelled.

TRUE/FALSE

52 Oscillations occur in amplifier systems due to the ____________ and ____________ of circuit components.

53 List two methods of reducing parasitic oscillations in power amplifiers.

54 Statement 1: Frequency distortion occurs in amplifier systems due to a shift in the quiescent point.
Statement 2: The shift in the quiescent point may be caused by the self capacitance and inductance of transistor electrodes.

(*a*) Only statement 1 is true
(*b*) Only statement 2 is true
(*c*) Both statements 1 and 2 are true
(*d*) Neither statement 1 nor 2 is true.

Underline the correct answer.

55 List the functions of the components in the push-pull a.f. power amplifier of Figure 51.

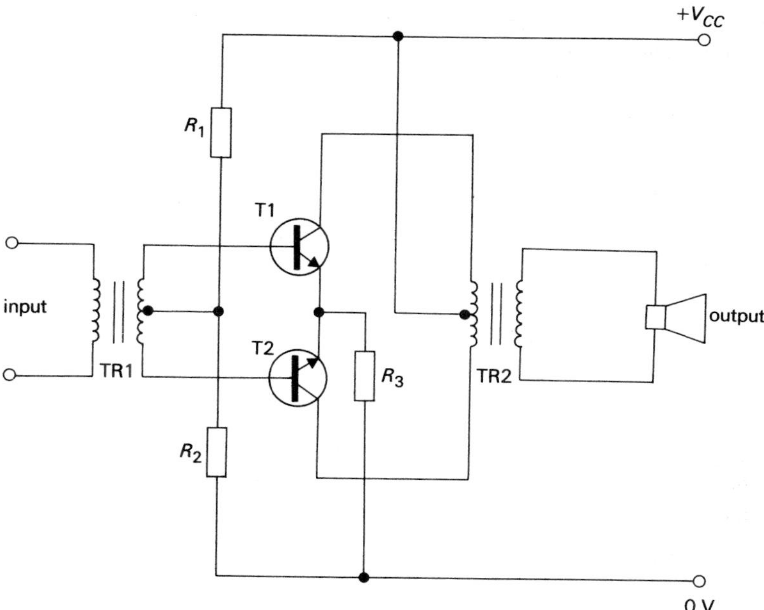

Figure 51 Circuit diagram for Self-assessment question 55

Topic area Noise

After reading the following material, the reader shall:

5 Know basic concepts of electrical noise and its relation to signa[l] strength.
5.1 Define noise as any unwanted signal.
5.2 List sources of external noise.
5.3 State precautions taken to minimize effects of external noise.
5.4 List sources of internal receiver noise.
5.5 State precautions taken to minimize effects of internal receiver nois[e].
5.6 Define signal-to-noise ratio in an amplifier or receiver.
5.7 Calculate signal-to-noise ratio in dB given signal and noise powe[r].

Electrical noise is spurious random generation of alternating voltage[s] in conductors and devices or electromagnetic radiation by externa[l] sources which is capable of transduction into alternating voltages.

In an electrical or electronic system (represented by the box in Figur[e] 52), there is an input and an output.

Solutions to self-assessment questions (pages 64–67)

44 Harmonic distortion occurs when the input signal is so large that the active device of the amplifier does not operate within the linear range of its characteristics.

45 It may be reduced in small signal amplifiers by operating in class A with a small magnitude input signal.

It may be reduced in large signal amplifiers by operating in a push-pull arrangement.

46
(i) Frequency distortion
(ii) Phase distortion
(iii) Intermodulation distortion.

47 (*a*) Only statement 1 is true.
Statement 2 should read: The theoretical efficiency of class A power amplifiers is 50 per cent.

48 A Complementary push-pull
B Push-pull
C Single ended

49 (*a*) Only statement 1 is true.
Statement 2 should read: Class B power amplifiers are utilized in battery operated equipment because the collector current is zero on 'no signal'.

50 TRUE.

51 TRUE.

52 Self capacitance, inductance.

53 Methods of reducing parasitic oscillations in power amplifiers include:
(i) Use short component leads
(ii) Closely space the component leads
(iii) Decouple the supply lines.

54 (*b*) Only statement 2 is true.
Statement 1 should read: Harmonic distortion occurs in amplifier systems due to a shift in the quiescent point.

55 With reference to Figure 51:
R_1 and R_2 provide the necessary quiescent base currents for transistors T1 and T2.
R_3 provides the required thermal stability.
TR2 is a centre tapped transformer which adds together each half cycle of the signal in the primary winding.
TR1 is a centre tapped transformer and acts as a phase splitter for the input signal.

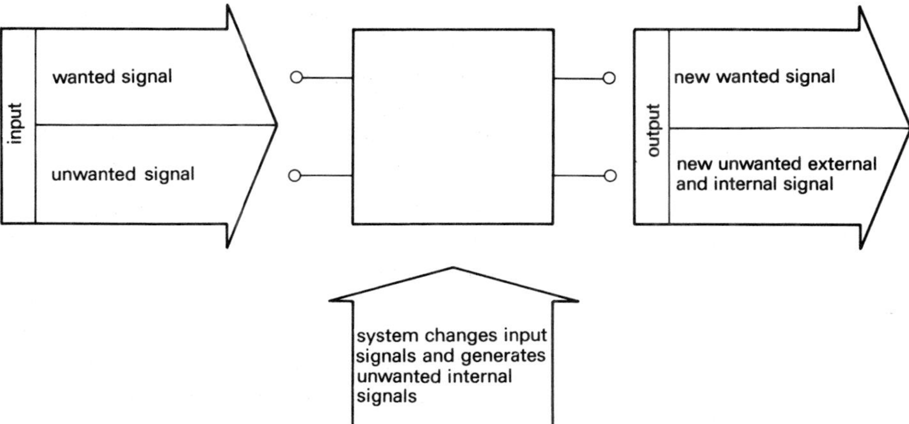

Figure 52 Sources of noise in an electrical or electronic system

In a perfect system no unwanted signals are introduced either internally or externally. In practice the unwanted signal exists even though it is desirable to remove it from most systems, e.g. the telephone communication system.

Definition: *Electrical noise* can be defined as any unwanted signal which is always present in an electrical or electronic system. An unwanted signal is called interference.

Sources of noise

(*a*) *External noise*

There are many sources which produce external electrical noise; they can be divided into two main groups.

Artificial: These sources are man-made and they very often have regular properties. The interference can occur due to sparking from apparatus and devices such as switches (for example from ignition systems). Also in this group can be included radio signals that are unwanted in the system. These can often be heard when listening to a receiver when one signal continually interferes with the reception of another signal.

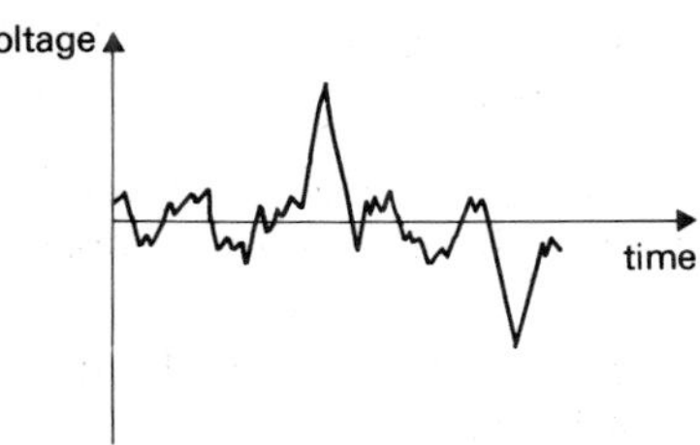

igure 53 Example of a waveform f naturally occurring external noise

Natural: These usually enter the system via an aerial system and have irregular properties as shown in Figure 53. This noise can originate in the atmosphere (e.g. electrical storms), or can be caused by cosmic electromagnetic radiation which comes from solar and galactic sources (i.e. the sun and the stars).

To minimize these unwanted effects a number of remedies can be suggested. These include:

Artificial: The interference that is caused from external electrical devices is suppressed at its source, if this is possible, using filters appropriate to the cause of interference. If a radio is to be fitted to a car, a number of sources of interference may need to be suppressed e.g. spark plugs and dynamo. The man-made radio signals that cause interference can be minimized by careful receiver design.

Natural: Solar noise can be reduced by pointing the antenna away from the source, or by altering the directional properties of the antenna. Galactic noise (from stars) can also be reduced by pointing the antenna away from the source. Also, it is found that this 'sky noise' reduces to a low order in the u.h.f. and s.h.f. bands (i.e. 300–30,000 MHz in the microwave band) as shown in Figure 54. Therefore when sky noise must be kept to a minimum, e.g. in radio astronomy and space communications, u.h.f. and s.h.f. bands are chosen. Atmospherics can be reduced by circuit design as in f.m. receivers (but not in a.m. systems).

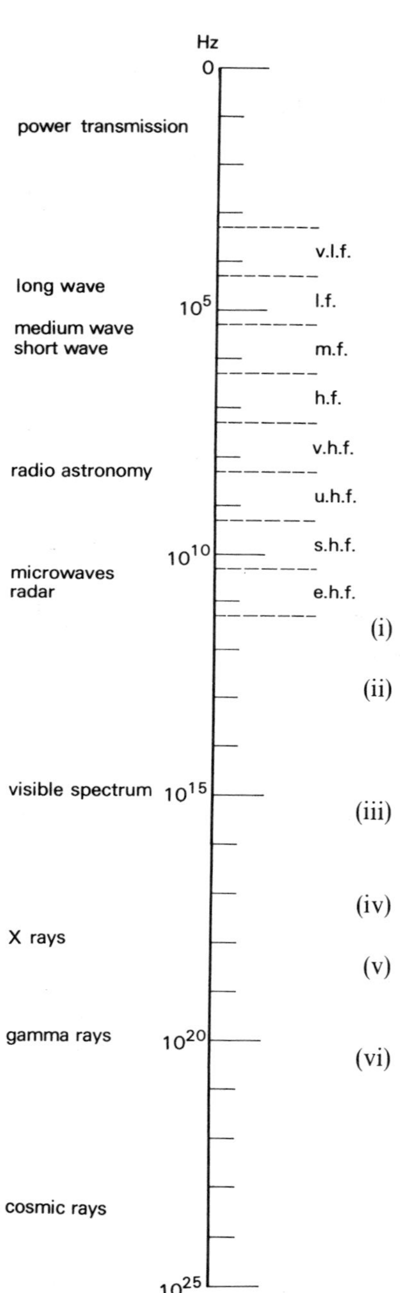

Figure 54 Electromagnetic spectrum

(*b*) *Internal noise*

A receiver is generally constructed from discrete components (transistors, resistors, capacitors, etc.) or from integrated circuits together with some discrete components. Noise can be generated by the following:

(i) *Thermal noise* (white noise) which is produced by the random motion of 'free' electrons in a conductor.

(ii) *Shot noise* which is produced by the random fluctuations in the emission of electrons from a cathode surface (e.g. valve) or by the random variations in the diffusion of charge carriers in a semiconductor diode or transistor.

(iii) *Partition noise* which is caused by the division of current to one or another electrodes in multigrid valves. This can also occur in transistors.

(iv) *Microphonic noise* which is caused by effects arising from mechanical vibration of circuit parts. This is reduced by careful circuit design.

(v) *Contact noise* which is caused by poor electrical contacts. This is reduced by keeping the number of contacts to a minimum, and by regular maintenance of the contacts.

(vi) *Hum* which is caused by voltages having their origin in associated or adjacent power supplies. This is reduced by careful circuit design.

Noise produced by causes (i), (ii) and (iii) can be reduced by a suitable choice of components and by operating equipment at low temperatures. It can also be shown that the noise level decreases in the v.h.f. and u.h.f. bands, but increases outside this range. Often the noise power in a system is required and must be based on the total value within some defined bandwidth. A summary of information is contained in Figure 55.

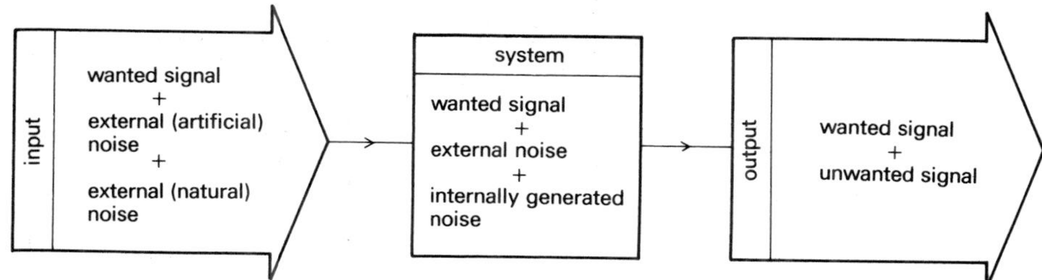

Figure 55 Summary of sources of noise in an electrical or electronic system

Signal-to-noise ratio

In amplifiers or receivers the input signals are of low power and accompanied by noise. Amplification is necessary and hence both signal and noise levels are increased, but the amplification circuitry also introduces further noise into the output. Consider two similar amplifiers each of which receives a wanted signal together with external noise as shown in Figure 56.

In the first case, Figure 56(*a*), the output signal includes the amplified signal together with the generated noise.

$\therefore X = 10(P_{in} + N_{ex}) + N_{gen}$ where X is the amplifier output

$\therefore X = 10\ P_{in} + (10N_{ex} + N_{gen})$

In the second case, Figure 56(*b*), assuming that the noise generated is the same in both cases, then

$Y = 10(2P_{in} + N_{ex}) + N_{gen}$ where Y is the amplifier output

$\therefore Y = 20\ P_{in} + (10N_{ex} + N_{gen})$

Table 3 has been constructed to show the comparison of the signal-to-noise ratios at the input and output of each system.

	input $\frac{\textit{signal power}}{\textit{noise power}}$	output $\frac{\textit{signal power}}{\textit{noise power}}$
first case	P_{in}/N_{ex}	$10P_{in}/(10N_{ex} + N_{gen})$
second case	$2P_{in}/N_{ex}$	$20P_{in}/(10N_{ex} + N_{gen})$

Table 3 Comparison of ratios

Note that the ratio in Table 3:

(i) is different at different points in the system
(ii) varies at a point in the system if the wanted input power is changed
(iii) varies at a point in the system if the input frequency is varied, because the gain of the amplifier is not constant for all frequencies.

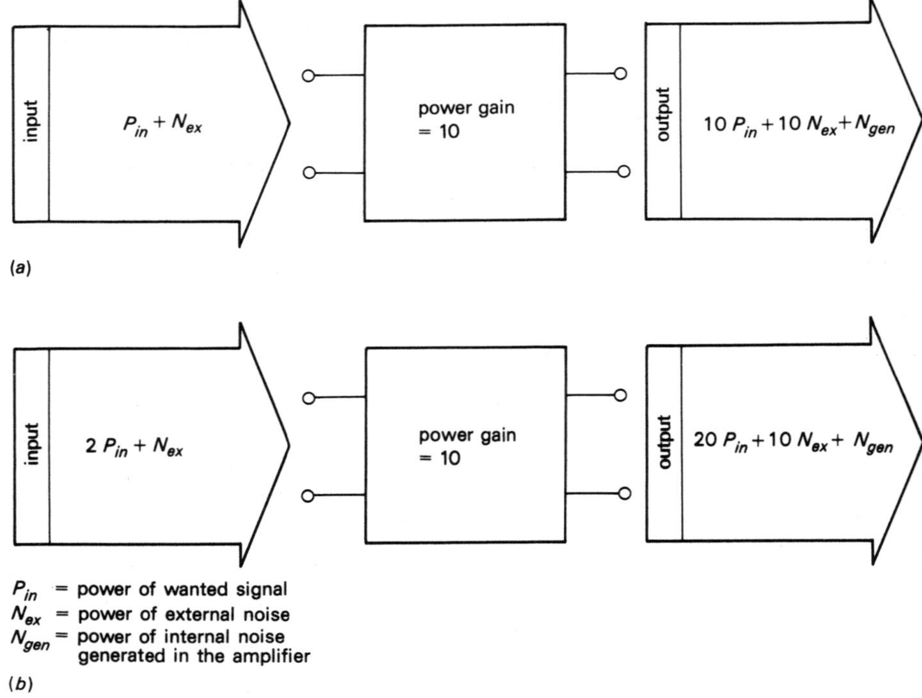

Figure 56 Comparison of amplifieıs with different wanted signal powers at the input

Two points must be remembered when quoting a signal-to-noise ratio for comparison of amplifiers:

(i) the point at which the ratio is to be measured must be stated

(ii) the input power and the bandwidth over which the gain is assumed constant must also be stated.

In practice the input to an amplifier or receiver (which is basically an amplifier and a tuner) contains a range of frequencies. Thus the bandwidth of information is quoted.

Definition: For a quoted input signal power, over a quoted bandwidth, the signal-to-noise ratio in an amplifier or receiver is given by

$$R = \frac{\text{average wanted signal power}}{\text{average noise power present}} = \frac{P}{N}$$

Signal-to-noise ratios are generally expressed in decibels which means that the above formula must be converted to logarithmic power form

$$R = 10\,\log_{10}\left(\frac{P}{N}\right)$$

The following examples use typical figures of noise levels to demonstrate how the ratios are used in practice.

Example 1

If the average wanted signal power at the input of an amplifier is 1 mW and the average noise power present is 10 μW, find the input signal-to-noise ratio in dB if the frequency of the input signal is 1 kHz.

$$R = 10 \log_{10}\left(\frac{1 \times 10^{-3}}{10 \times 10^{-6}}\right) \text{ dB}$$

$$\therefore R = 10 \log_{10} 100 \text{ dB}$$

$$\therefore R = 20 \text{ dB at 1 kHz for an input power of 1·01 mW}$$

(1 mW + 10 μW)

In the electronics industry, voltages are used and thus the signal-to-noise ratio becomes:

$$R = \frac{V_s^2/Z}{V_n^2/Z}$$ where V_s = voltage of wanted signal
V_n = voltage of noise present
Z = impedance at point

If Z is assumed to be the same for both signals then

$$R = \left(\frac{V_s}{V_n}\right)^2$$

$$\therefore R = 10 \log_{10}\left(\frac{V_s}{V_n}\right)^2 \text{ dB}$$

$$\therefore R = 20 \log_{10}\left(\frac{V_s}{V_n}\right) \text{ dB}$$

Example 2

For an input signal of 5 μV, over the mid-band gain of an amplifier, the output has a wanted signal of 200 mV and a noise output of 5 mV. What is the signal-to-noise ratio at the output of the amplifier?

Signal-to-noise ratio at the output $= 20 \log_{10}\left(\frac{200}{5}\right) = 32 \text{ dB}$

for an input signal of 5 μV over the mid-band gain.

Self-assessment questions

1 Define the term electrical noise.

2 List three sources of external artificial noise.

3 List three sources of external natural noise.

4 State the precautions that are taken to minimize the effects of external artificial and natural noise.

5 List three sources of internal receiver noise.

6 State the precautions that are taken to minimize the effects of internal receiver noise.

7 Define the signal-to-noise ratio of an amplifier.

8 Calculate the signal-to-noise ratio in dB for the average wanted signal powers, and the average noise powers present listed in Table 4. Use the values to complete the table.

	P(mW)	N(μW)	R (dB)
1	1	0·1	
2	2	2·0	
3	4	40	
4	10	1000	
5	2	4000	

Table 4

9 The average wanted input power to an amplifier, and the average external noise power present, are measured as 2mW and 1μW respectively. The power gain of the amplifier is found to be constant over the frequency range 0–100 kHz and is measured at 20. The average noise power generated within the amplifier is measured at the output as 0·1 mW. Calculate the signal-to-noise ratio at the input and the output of the amplifier.

10 The total average power measured at the input of an amplifier is 2·002 mW. The average noise power generated within the amplifier is measured at the output as 0·2 mW. All measurements are made over the frequency range 100Hz–1MHz (for which the gain of the amplifier is 25) and for the input power quoted. The wanted signal is measured at the output of the amplifier as 50 mW. Calculate

(*a*) External noise at the input of the amplifier
(*b*) Signal-to-noise ratio at the input of the amplifier
(*c*) Total noise at the output of the amplifier
(*d*) Signal-to-noise ratio at the output of the amplifier.

Topic area Feedback

After reading the following material, the reader shall:

6 Understand the general principles of feedback.
6.1 Draw a block diagram of a basic feedback amplifier.
6.2 Derive the general expression for stage gain of a basic feedback amplifier.
6.3 Distinguish the terms inversion and phase shift in relation to the input and output signals of a feedback amplifier.
6.4 Define positive and negative feedback.
6.5 Explain the practical interpretation of the general expression for the stage gain derived in **6.2.**

In the past, design and development of electronic circuitry was based around the valve and the transistor as a unit. Since the advent of the integrated circuit, and the introduction of a cheap, high gain, wideband amplifier, another design technique has become more important whereby the amplifier is made the unit around which the design procedure is based. This is not a new technique, but it is important as more and more devices become part of the integrated circuit technology.

As was briefly indicated in Electronics 2, if some of the output signal of an amplifier is fed back into the input, the operational behaviour of the total unit (amplifier together with feedback) can be made quite different from that of the amplifier operating with no feedback applied. The way in which the unit behaves depends on the type of feedback and the amount of feedback applied to the input.

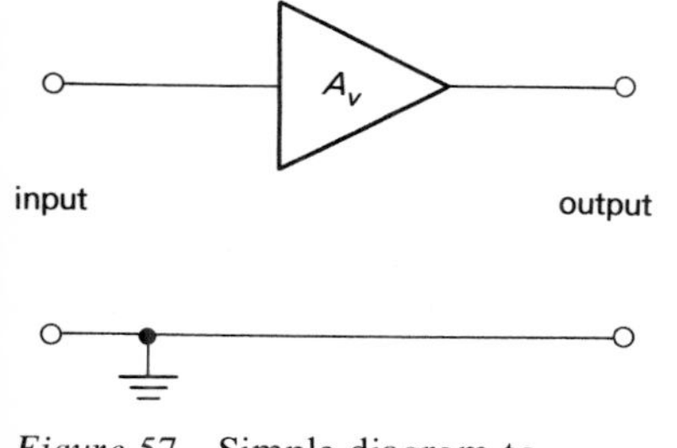

Figure 57 Simple diagram to represent an amplifier

The unit can be made to operate as a variety of different types of amplifier, each with different characteristics, e.g. a high quality voltage amplifier, a buffer amplifier, or even as an oscillator when the required frequency determining network is included.

This design procedure means that it is more convenient to use a circuit symbol for the amplifier itself (rather than a collection of circuit symbols), where the input and output terminals are the only connections to the device. One convention used to represent the amplifier is shown in Figure 57. The earth connection shown is usually omitted in circuit diagrams. Thus a single input amplifier is represented as shown in Figure 58. The letter A is used to represent the gain of the amplifier. In particular the voltage gain is represented by A_v where

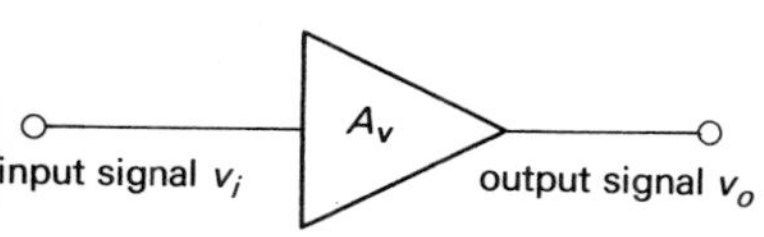

Figure 58 Diagram to represent an amplifier, further simplified

$$A_v = \frac{v_0}{v_L} \qquad (1)$$

Solutions to self-assessment questions (pages 73–74)

1 Electrical noise can be defined as any unwanted signal which is always present in an electrical or electronic system.

2–6 See Table 5.

7 For a quoted input signal power, over a quoted bandwidth, the signal-to-noise ratio is

$$\frac{\text{average wanted signal power}}{\text{average noise power present}}$$

8

(1) $R = 10 \log_{10}\dfrac{1 \times 10^{-3}}{0{\cdot}1 \times 10^{-6}}$

$= 10 \log_{10} 10\,000 = 40$ dB

(2) $R = 10 \log_{10}\dfrac{2 \times 10^{-3}}{2 \times 10^{-6}}$

$= 10 \log_{10} 1000 = 30$ dB

(3) $R = 10 \log_{10}\dfrac{4 \times 10^{-3}}{40 \times 10^{-6}}$

$= 10 \log_{10} 100 = 20$ dB

(4) $R = 10 \log_{10}\dfrac{10 \times 10^{-3}}{1000 \times 10^{-6}}$

$= 10 \log_{10} 10 = 10$ dB

(5) $R = 10 \log_{10}\dfrac{2 \times 10^{-3}}{4000 \times 10^{-6}}$

$= 10 \log_{10}(\frac{1}{2}) = -10 \log_{10}(\frac{2}{1})$

$= -3$ dB

The negative sign indicates an attenuation from which Table 4 may be completed.

Sources of noise	Precautions to minimize the effects
Sparking plug (ingition systems)	Carbon loads or suppression caps
Motor commutator (dynamo)	Capacitor suppression
Switches	Make before break
Electric shavers	Capacitor suppression
Vacuum cleaner	Capacitor suppression
Unwanted radio signal	Circuit design to increase sensitivity
Sun	Alter directional properties of antenna
Stars	Re-set direction of antenna
Atmospherics	Use appropriate circuitry e.g. f.m. receiver
Thermal noise in a conductor	Choose components with low noise properties, or operate at low temperatures
Shot noise in a diode	
Partition noise in a transistor	
Microphonic noise in a valve	Use special mechanical supports
Contact noise in a poor electrical contact	Reduce number of contacts e.g. incorporate ICs
Hum due to stray magnetic pick up	Use batteries or careful design of component layout

Table 5 Answers to Questions 2–6

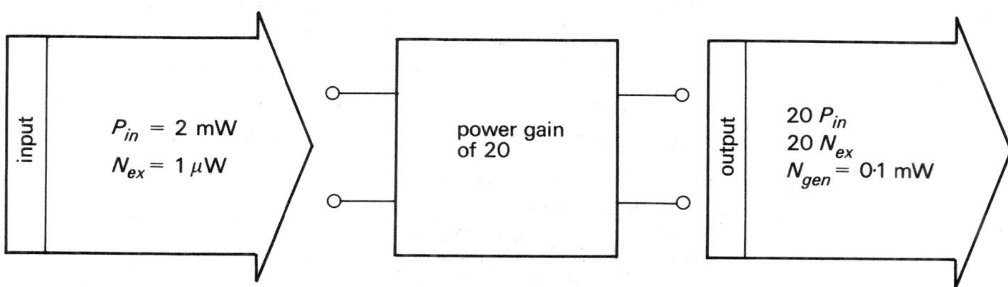

Figure 59 Amplifier for Self-assessment question 9

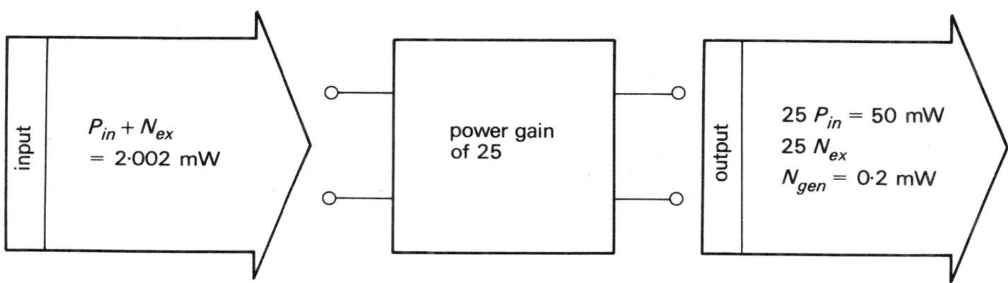

Figure 60 Amplifier for Self-assessment question 10

9 From Figure 59,

At input $R = 10 \log_{10} \frac{2 \times 10^{-3}}{1 \times 10^{-6}}$

$= 10 \log_{10} 2000$

$= 33$ dB

At output

wanted signal power $= 20\ P_{in}$

$= 40$ mW

noise power $= 20\ N_{ex} + N_{gen}$

$= 20(1 \times 10^{-6}) + 0{\cdot}1 \times 10^{-3}$W

$= 120\ \mu$W

$$R = 10 \log_{10} \frac{40 \times 10^{-3}}{120 \times 10^{-6}}$$

$= 10 \log_{10} 333{\cdot}3 = 25{\cdot}2$ dB

These signal-to-noise ratios are quoted for an input power of 2·001 mW over the frequency range 0–100 kHz.

10

(*a*) From Figure 60, at the output:

$25\ P_{in} = 50 \times 10^{-3}$

$\therefore\ P_{in} = 2$ mW

At the input:

$P_{in} + N_{ex} = 2{\cdot}002$ mW

$\therefore\ N_{ex} = (2{\cdot}002 - 2)$ mW

$\therefore\ N_{ex} = 2\ \mu$W

(*b*) At the input:

$$R = 10 \log_{10} \frac{2 \times 10^{-3}}{2 \times 10^{-6}} = 30 \text{dB}$$

(*c*) At the output:

total external noise $= 25 \times 2\ \mu$W

$\therefore$ total noise $= (200 + 50)\ \mu$W

$= 250\ \mu$W

(*d*) At the output:

$$R = 10 \log_{10} \frac{50 \times 10^{-3}}{250 \times 10^{-6}} = 23 \text{ dB}$$

These signal-to-noise ratios are quoted for an input power of 2·002 μW over the frequency range 100 Hz to 1 MHz.

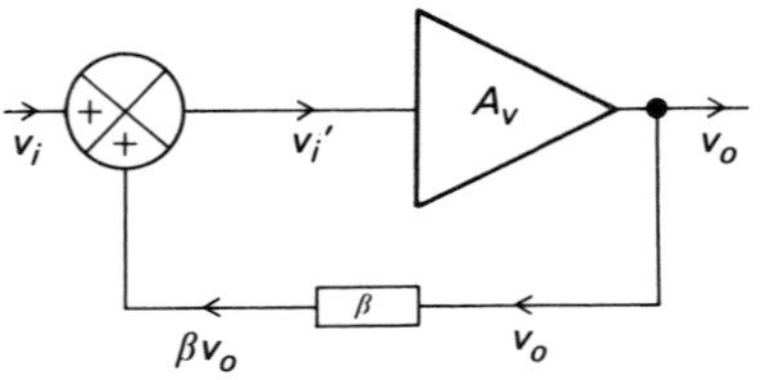

Figure 61 Block diagram of a basic feedback amplifier

The various properties of a single input amplifier such as gain, input and output impedance are fixed when the amplifier is manufactured. However, the gain can be reduced by positioning resistive attenuators either in front of or following the amplifier. Input and output impedances can be increased or reduced by using series or shunt resistors respectively, connected to the relevant terminals, but only at the expense of *signal power.*

One method of avoiding the waste of signal power, yet still varying these properties, is to feed some of the output signal from the amplifier back into the input circuit, as shown in Figure 61. The symbols used in Figure 61 are explained in Figure 62.

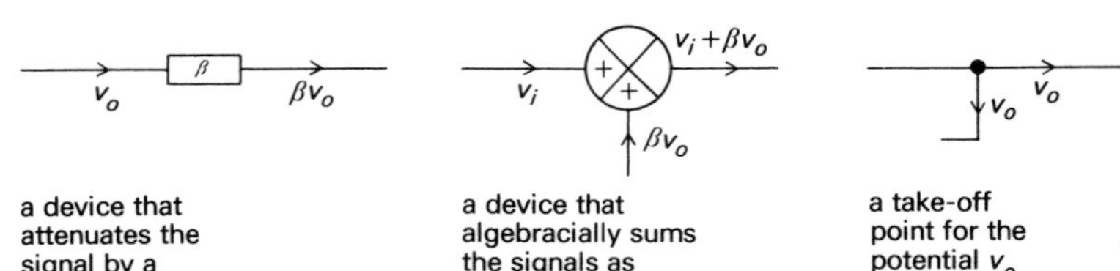

Figure 62 Symbols and their meanings

The use of symbols allows the designer to analyse the system without having to consider all the individual circuit elements.

In Figure 61 the voltage at the input to the amplifier is given by

$$v_i^1 = v_i + \beta v_0 \qquad (2)$$

From equation 1 the voltage gain $A_v = \dfrac{v_0}{v_i^1}$ (3)

Substituting equation 2 into 3 gives $A_v = \dfrac{v_0}{v_i + \beta v_0}$

$$\therefore\ A_v(v_i + \beta v_0) = v_0$$

$$\therefore\ A_v v_i + A_v \beta v_0 = v_0$$

$$\therefore\ A_v v_i = v_0(1 - A_v \beta)$$

$$\therefore\ \frac{v_0}{v_i} = \frac{A_v}{1 - A_v \beta}$$

This is the voltage gain of the system with feedback and is represented by G_v

$$\therefore \text{ voltage gain of system } G_v = \frac{A_v}{1 - A_v \beta} \qquad (4)$$

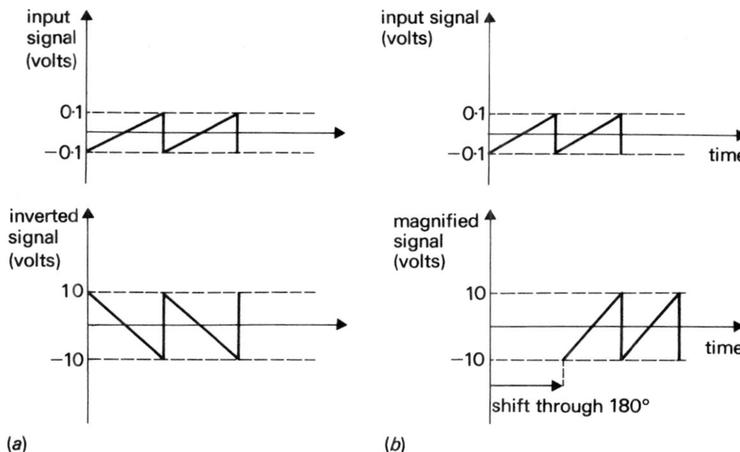

Figure 63 Difference between inverted and 180° phase shifted signal

When a signal passes from the input to the output of a system each circuit element affects the signal. If the system contains a transistor (or a valve) used in an amplifier (with the associated resistors, capacitors and perhaps inductors), the transistor (or valve) causes the signal to be inverted. This is not the same as shifting the signal through 180° as is shown by Figure 63.

Figure 63(*a*) shows a triangular waveshape and the resultant waveshape produced by both a magnification of 100 and an inversion.

Figure 63(*b*) shows a triangular waveshape and the resultant waveshape produced by both a magnification of 100 and a phase shift of 180°. The two resultant waveshapes are not the same.

Figure 64 shows the same effect when a sinewave is assumed to be the input waveshape. When only one cycle of the input is considered, the distinction between inversion and phase shift is clear. However when more than one cycle is considered this distinction becomes blurred.

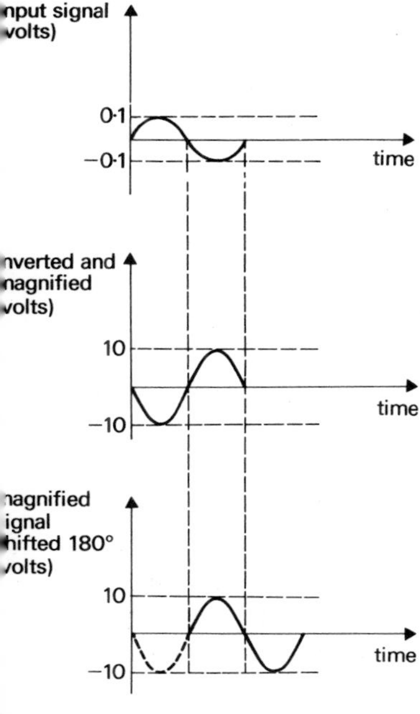

igure 64 Difference between
nverted and 180° phase shifted sine
vave signal

In Figure 61, the signal v_i^1 on passing through the amplifier is inverted. When more than one amplifying stage is used reactive components may be used to connect the stages together. Alternatively, if the input frequency is varied, different reactive components may begin to operate. The feedback network itself may also contain reactive components. Thus at some frequencies the input signal to the system may not be in phase with the input signal to the amplifier. Similarly the output signal applied to the summing device may not be in phase with the output signal of the amplifier. Also as the frequency changes so will this phase shift. Because of this it may well become exceedingly difficult at these frequencies to decide if the signal fed back to the summing device tends to aid or to oppose the input signal.

For the analysis at this level only identifiable cases will be considered where amplifiers invert and the feedback network is used to invert the signal where necessary.

If the signal fed back *aids* the input signal, *positive* feedback is said to be applied.

If the signal fed back *opposes* the input signal, *negative* feedback is said to be applied.

In practice two types of circuits are used to provide a negative feedback type of amplifier:

(*a*) an *inverting* amplifier with a *resistive* feedback network
(*b*) a *non-inverting* amplifier with a *transformer* in the feedback loop.

The non-inverting amplifier can be made by connecting two inverting amplifiers together in series.

At this point it is worth remembering that when a signal is inverted its sign changes

e.g.	signal	inverted signal
	$v = 10$ volts	$-v = -10$ volts
	$v = 10 \sin\omega t$ volts	$-v = -10 \sin\omega t$ volts

This means for the amplifier gain equation (1) that:
(*a*) for an inverting amplifier $v_0 = -A_v v_i$
(*b*) for a non-inverting amplifier $v_0 = A_v v_i$

Consider the effect of using either of these amplifiers in the general feedback system shown in Figure 61, and described by equation 4.

(*a*) *Inverting amplifier* $v_0 = -A_v v_i$

$$\therefore \frac{v_0}{v_i} = -A_v$$

For a resistive network β is positive

$$\therefore \text{Substituting in equation 4} \quad G_v = \frac{(-A_v)}{1-(-A_v)(\beta)}$$

$$\therefore G_v = -\frac{A_v}{1 + A_v\beta}$$

Compared with an amplifier without feedback, the gain is reduced because $1 + A_v\beta$ is greater than 1. However the system (which contains the amplifier with feedback) still inverts the input signal to the system, at the output of the system as shown by the minus sign.

(*b*) *Non-inverting amplifier* $v_0 = A_v v_i$

$$\therefore \frac{v_0}{v_i} = A_v$$

If the feedback network uses a transformer to provide the feedback fraction, then for negative feedback the transformer is connected such that β is negative.

$$\therefore\ G_v = \frac{A_v}{1-(A_v)(-\beta)}$$

$$\therefore\ G_v = +\frac{A_v}{1+A_v\beta}$$

Thus compared with an amplifier without feedback the gain is reduced because $1+A_v\beta$ is greater than 1. However the system (which contains the amplifier with feedback) does not invert the input signal to the system at the output as shown by the plus sign.

In fact these results are to be expected by considering the type of feedback applied. Negative feedback opposes the input signal, and thus reduces the total magnitude of the input signal. This in turn reduces the gain.

The general expression for the voltage gain of a negative feedback system using either an inverting or non-inverting amplifier is given by

$$G_v = \pm\frac{A_v}{1+A_v\beta}$$

The sign must be chosen according to the type of amplifier which is used. The terms in the above formula are called by the following names:

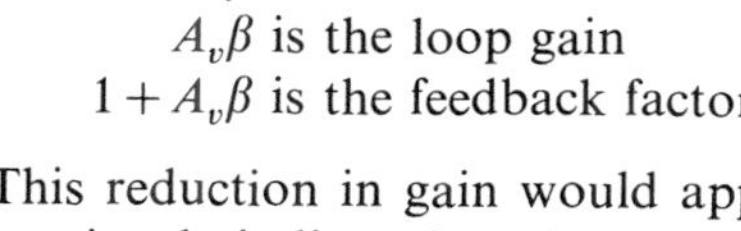

A_v is the open loop gain
β is the feedback fraction
$A_v\beta$ is the loop gain
$1+A_v\beta$ is the feedback factor

This reduction in gain would appear to be pointless. However, as previously indicated, various properties of the amplifier need to be changed for specific design purposes. The effect of negative feedback on these properties is considered in the next section.

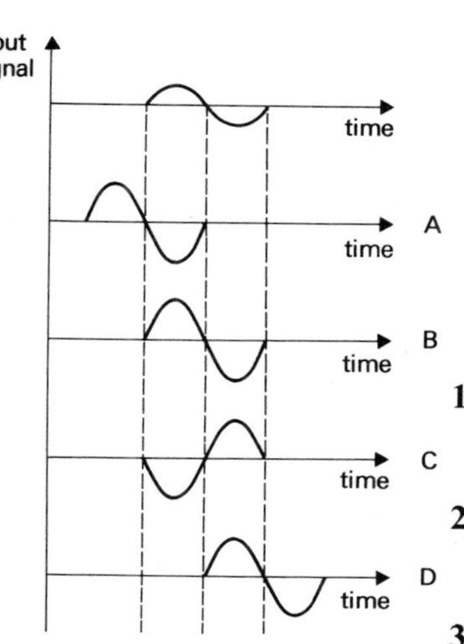

igure 65 Graph for Self-assessment uestion 3

Self-assessment questions

1 Draw a block diagram of a basic feedback amplifier. The diagram should include a 'summing' device.

2 For the block diagram shown in Figure 61, derive the general expression for the stage gain of a basic feedback amplifier.

3 The diagrams drawn in Figure 65 show an input signal and four output signals. Tick the output signal that is obtained from an inverting amplifier.

4 Which of the following statements relating to negative feedback amplifiers are true?

(*a*) The output signal of an inverting amplifier is 180° out of phase relative to the input signal

(*b*) Reactive components cause a phase shift of a signal as it passes through them

(*c*) The feedback device never contains reactive components

(*d*) The gain of an amplifier is changed by the application of feedback.

5 The four sentences which follow relate to a feedback amplifier. Delete the incorrect word in each sentence.

(*a*) If the signal fed back aids/opposes the input signal, positive feedback is said to be applied.

(*b*) If the signal fed back aids/opposes the input signal negative feedback is said to be applied.

(*c*) If an inverting amplifier is to be used as a negative feedback amplifier, a resistive/transformer feedback network must be used.

(*d*) If a non-inverting amplifier is to be used as a negative feedback amplifier, a resistive/transformer feedback network must be used.

6 Match the terms in the right hand column of Table 6 to the symbols given in the left hand column.

	symbol	term
A	A_v	1 loop gain
B	β	2 feedback factor
C	$1+A_v\beta$	3 feedback fraction
D	$A_v\beta$	4 open loop gain

A	
B	
C	
D	

Table 6

After reading the following material, the reader shall:

6.6 State the effects of applying negative feedback to an amplifier in relation to:

(*a*) gain

(*b*) gain stability

(*c*) bandwidth

(*d*) distortion

(*e*) noise

(*f*) input and output resistances.

6.7 Apply feedback principles to practical circuits.

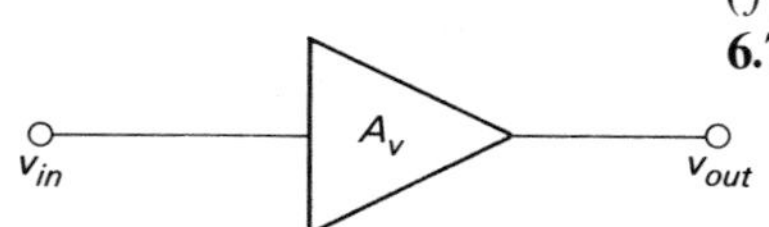

Figure 66 Simple amplifier representation

In Figure 66 the amplifier has a voltage gain

$$A_v = -\frac{v_{out}}{v_{in}}$$

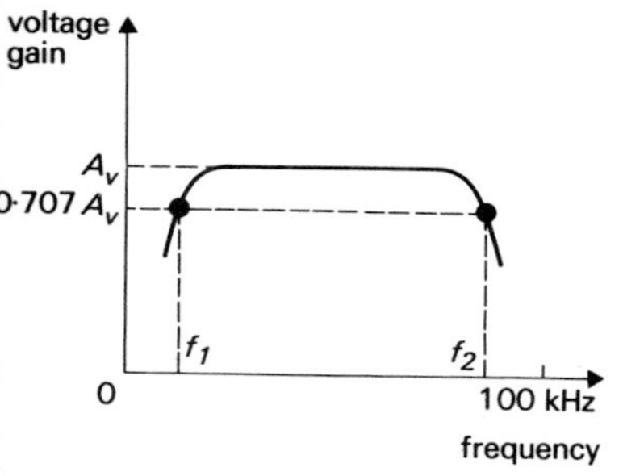

Figure 67 Bandwidth for simple amplifier

The gain may change due to changes in, for example, supply voltage, ageing or environmental effects, especially temperature.

A requirement of an amplifier might be to amplify, with a constant voltage gain, all voltages over a given frequency range, for example 0–100 kHz. In practice, the amplifier cannot fulfil this requirement due to the effects of circuit reactance near both the lower end and the higher end of the frequency range. As shown in Figure 67 the bandwidth is less than the required specifications.

However some improvements may be obtained by applying negative feedback to the amplifier, as shown in the following example.

If numbers rather than symbols are used, the effect of negative feedback is more easily seen. Assume the amplifier is inverting and has an open loop gain of 57 dB when first manufactured. A purely resistive feedback loop is then connected such that the feedback fraction is $\frac{1}{30}$. Calculate the gain of the system.

$$\text{Amplifier gain in dB} = 20 \log_{10} \frac{v_{out}}{v_{in}} = 20 \log_{10} A_v$$

$$\therefore 57 = 20 \log_{10} A_v$$

$$\therefore A_v = 708$$

This answer is quoted as a magnitude only and for the next part the sign must be considered i.e. inverting or non-inverting amplifier.

$$\text{Now gain of system } G_v = -\frac{A_v}{1 + A_v\beta} \quad \text{(negative to show inverting amplifier)}$$

$$\therefore G_v = -\frac{708}{1 + 708(\frac{1}{30})} = -28{\cdot}8$$

The effect of including a resistive feedback loop is to reduce the gain considerably.

As suggested previously, the signal fed back opposes the input signal (negative feedback). The output signal is reduced, and hence the effect of applying negative feedback is to reduce the gain.

If after five years the gain of the amplifier without feedback has fallen to 40 dB (a valve amplifier due to ageing, or an IC amplifier due to exposure to external radiation, say) and the value of β remains constant, calculate the gain of the system.

$$\text{Amplifier gain in dB} = 20 \log_{10} A_v$$

$$\therefore 40 = 20 \log_{10} A_v$$

$$\therefore A_v = 100$$

Thus without feedback, after five years, the amplifier gain has fallen from 708 to 100.

Solutions to self-assessment questions (pages 81–82)

1 A block diagram of a basic feedback amplifier is shown in Figure 68.

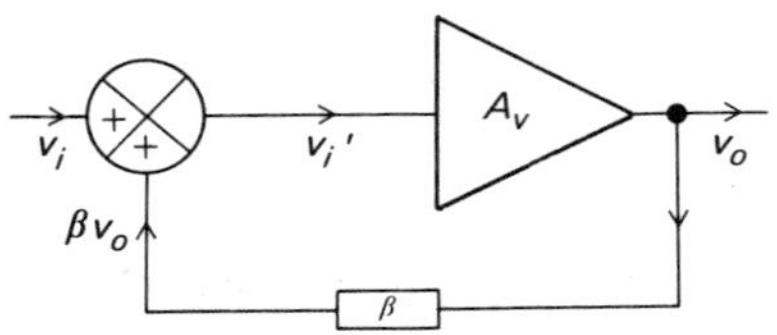

Figure 68 Solution to Self-assessment question 1

2 The general expression $A_v = \frac{A_v}{1+A_v\beta}$ is derived on page 78.

3 Diagram (*c*) is the output signal of an inverting amplifier.

4 Statement (*b*) is the only statement which is true.
Statement (*d*) is false because the gain of the system varies; the gain of the amplifier does not.

5
(*a*) the word *opposes* should be deleted
(*b*) the word *aids* should be deleted
(*c*) the word *transformer* should be deleted
(*d*) the word *resistor* should be deleted.

6

A	4
B	3
C	2
D	1

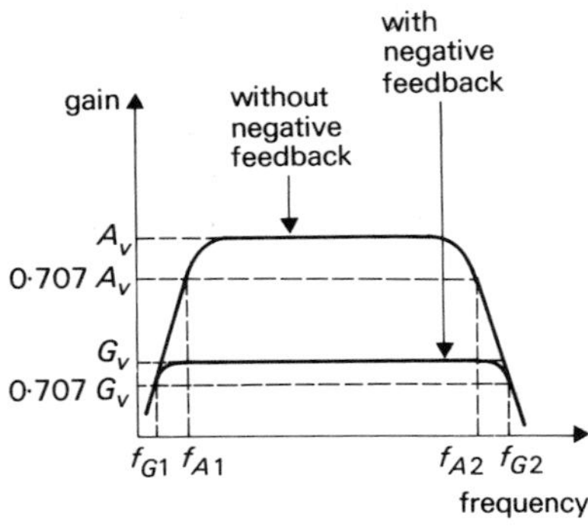

Figure 69 Gain of amplifier with and without negative feedback connected

Also $G_v = -\frac{A_v}{1+A_v\beta}$

$$\therefore G_v = -\frac{100}{1+100(\frac{1}{30})} = -23{\cdot}1$$

With feedback the system gain has fallen from 28·1 to 23·1.

This means that over a period of five years if the amplifier had been designed to operate without feedback its gain would have fallen from 708 to 100.

However when negative feedback is introduced the gain falls only from 28·8 to 23·1 over the same five year period. Thus one advantage of negative feedback is to reduce very noticeably the effects of ageing by stabilizing the gain of the system.

Consider the feedback formula

$$G_v = \pm\frac{A_v}{1+A_v\beta}$$

If the system is arranged such that

$$A_v\beta \gg 1$$

then $1+A_v\beta \approx A_v\beta$

$$\therefore G_v = \pm\frac{A_v}{A_v\beta} = \pm\frac{1}{\beta}$$

For a system where $A_v\beta$ is very much greater than unity, the gain of the system does not depend upon the open loop gain A_v but only upon the feedback fraction. If an inverting amplifier is used, and β is derived from the output using two high stability resistors, then

$$G_v = -\frac{1}{\beta}$$

Thus the gain is stable and independent of variations of supply voltage, ageing and environmental effects.

The effect on the bandwidth when negative feedback is applied is shown in Figure 69. The reduction in gain at the low end of the passband is due to the coupling methods used in a.c. amplifiers, as described in the topic area Amplifiers. The reduction at the high end of the passband is due to the change in reactance of the stray capacitances which shunt the output of the amplifier. Thus the gain is reduced by the application of negative feedback, but the bandwidth is increased.

As indicated in the topic area Noise, electrical noise may be generated in the amplifier itself. These unwanted signals are required to be kept as small as possible.

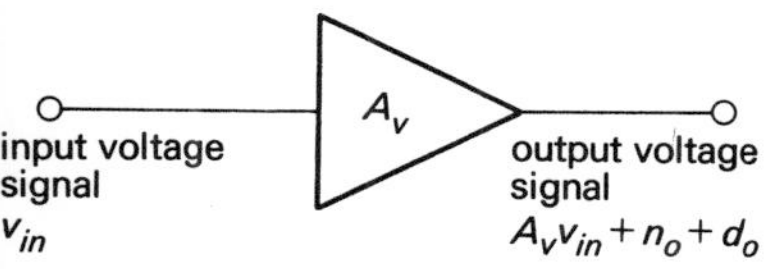

Figure 70 Amplifier with no feedback applied

Similarly the amplifier can distort the signal as it passes from input to output. This effect must be kept as small as possible, and one method by which it is achieved is by applying negative feedback.

Consider the amplifier shown in Figure 70, where no feedback is applied.

$$\text{output voltage signal} = A_v v_{in} + n_0 + d_0 \quad (5)$$

where n_0 represents signal introduced by amplifier as noise
d_0 represents signal introduced by amplifier as distortion

Consider this amplifier with feedback applied as shown in Figure 71.

$$\text{output voltage signal} = v_0 + N_0 + D_0$$

where N_0 represents signal introduced by amplifier as noise
D_0 represents signal introduced by amplifier as distortion

$$\text{feedback voltage} = \beta(v_0 + N_0 + D_0)$$

$$\text{input voltage to amplifier} = v_s + \beta(v_0 + N_0 + D_0) \quad (6)$$

where v_s is the voltage amplitude of the input signal

Substituting (6) into (5) gives

$$\text{output voltage signal} = A_v[v_s + \beta(v_0 + N_0 + D_0)] + n_0 + d_0$$

$$\therefore v_0 + N_0 + D_0 = A_v[v_s + \beta(v_0 + N_0 + D_0)] + n_0 + d_0$$

On rearranging this can be shown to be

$$v_0 + N_0 + D_0 = \frac{A_v}{1 - A_v\beta} v_s + \frac{n_0}{1 - A_v\beta} + \frac{d_0}{1 - A_v\beta} \quad (7)$$

Comparing equation 7 with equation 5 it can be seen that, not only is the output signal changed by the factor $\frac{1}{1 - A_v\beta}$, but so are the noise and distortion components. If *negative* feedback is applied, the factor becomes $\frac{1}{1 + A_v\beta}$, and the noise and distortion components are further reduced by this factor.

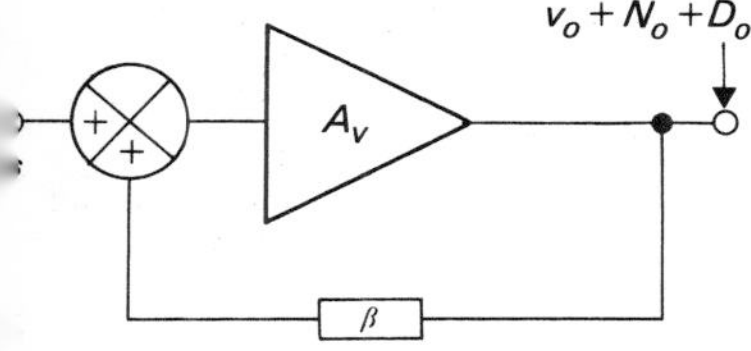

Figure 71 The same amplifier with negative feedback applied

Example 1

The open loop gain of an inverting amplifier is 150; the particular distortion content is 5%. Find the new distortion content when negative feedback is applied via a resistive network such that $\beta = 0{\cdot}1$.

$$D_0 = d_0 \frac{1}{1 + A_v\beta}$$

$$\therefore D_0 = 5 \frac{1}{1 + 150(0{\cdot}1)}\ \%$$

$$\therefore D_0 = \tfrac{5}{16}\%$$

Hence the distortion content is reduced from 5% to $\frac{5}{16}$%.

It must also be noted that an amplifier has an input and an output impedance. To transfer maximum signal power from one unit to another these impedances should be matched. Thus for example a pre-amplifier output impedance should be matched to an amplifier input impedance, as should the output impedance of the amplifier be matched to the input impedance of the next stage. This is one example where it may be necessary to change the impedance of an amplifier at either the input or output. It can be done by applying negative feedback.

The feedback can be taken from the output circuit in two ways:

(i) by making the feedback proportional to output voltage (called voltage feedback)

(ii) by making the feedback proportional to output current (called current feedback)

Similarly the feedback can be fed back into the input circuit in two ways; either in series or in shunt.

The names that apply to the four possible combinations are shown in Figure 72.

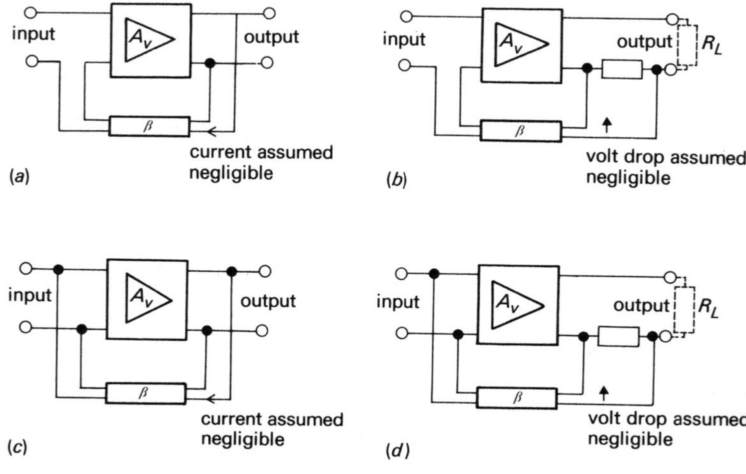

Figure 72 Methods of applying feedback
(a) series voltage feedback
(b) series current feedback
(c) shunt voltage feedback
(d) shunt current feedback

To analyse the effect of applying *negative* feedback as shown, and hence obtain the effective input and output impedances (resistances), is beyond the level of the present TEC objectives. It can be shown that applying negative feedback changes the input and output impedances; the results are summarized in Table 7.

type of negative feedback	input impedance (resistance)	output impedance (resistance)
series voltage	increases	decreases
shunt voltage	decreases	decreases
series current	increases	increases
shunt current	decreases	increases

Table 7

The results previously obtained can also be summarized.

Applying negative feedback causes

(i) Gain to reduce by a factor $\dfrac{1}{1+A_v\beta}$

(ii) Gain stability to increase

(iii) Bandwidth to increase

(iv) Distortion to reduce by a factor $\dfrac{1}{1+A_v\beta}$

(v) Noise to reduce by a factor $\dfrac{1}{1+A_v\beta}$

Hence, amplifiers are designed to have higher gains than would normally be required, so that a large amount of negative feedback can be applied. The result is a higher quality output.

Application of feedback principles to practical circuits

The advantages to be gained from applying negative feedback to an amplifier include:

(*a*) modification of input and output impedances
(*b*) reduction in noise and distortion
(*c*) stabilization of amplifier gain against external changes
(*d*) control of the frequency response of the amplifier
(*e*) control and stabilization of the d.c. operating conditions.

It is now proposed to relate applications to these five advantages.

(*i*) *Relationship between the resistances used in a resistive feedbac network and the feedback fraction*

In the resistive network used in the potential divider as shown in Figure 73

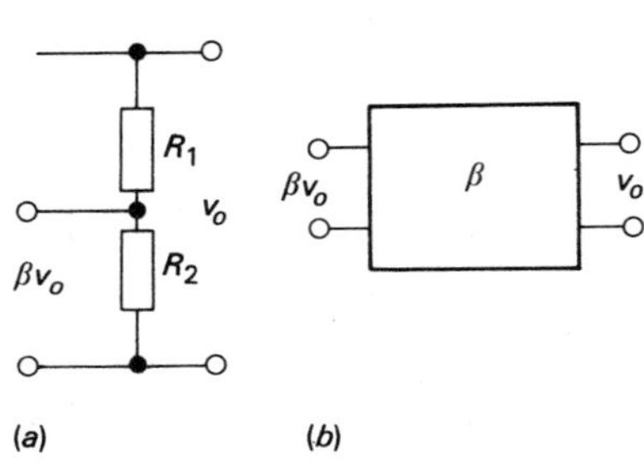

Figure 73 Diagram for feedback fraction

$$\text{current flowing through } R_1 \text{ and } R_2 = \frac{v_0}{R_1 + R_2}$$

$\therefore$ voltage across R_2 = current × resistance

$$= \frac{v_0}{(R_1 + R_2)} R_2$$

By comparison of Figure 73(*a*) and (*b*)

$$\beta = \frac{R_2}{R_1 + R_2}$$

(*ii*) *Calculation of the gain of an amplifying system where negative feedbac is applied using either a resistive network or a transformer*

Example 2

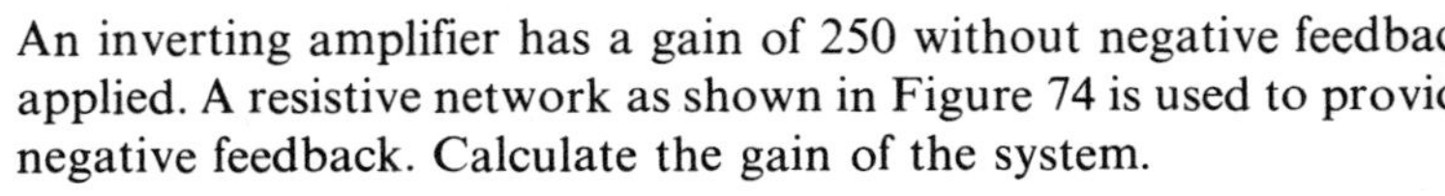
An inverting amplifier has a gain of 250 without negative feedbac applied. A resistive network as shown in Figure 74 is used to provid negative feedback. Calculate the gain of the system.

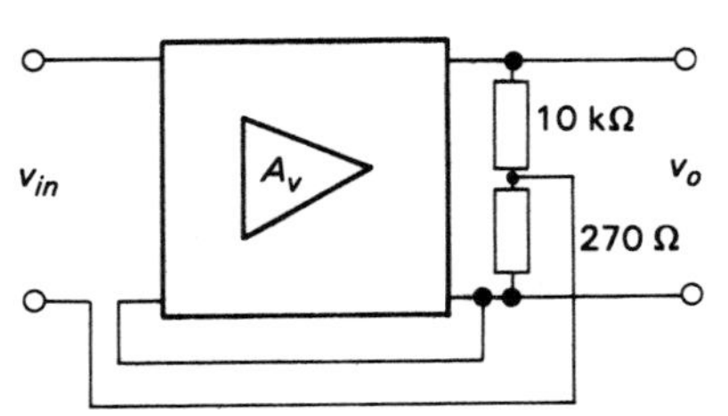

Figure 74 Negative feedback using a resistive network

Using the nomenclature of Figure 73, $R_1 = 10$ kΩ and $R_2 = 270$ Ω

$$\therefore \quad \beta = \frac{270}{270 + 10\,000} = 0{\cdot}026$$

$$\therefore \quad G_v = -\frac{250}{1 + 250(0{\cdot}026)} = -33$$ (minus sign to denote inverting amplifier)

Example 3

A non-inverting amplifier has a gain of 250 without negative feedbac applied. The feedback signal is taken as shown in Figure 75. Calculat the gain of the system.

$R_1 = 10$ kΩ and $R_2 = 270$ Ω as before

$\therefore \beta = 0{\cdot}026$

$$\therefore G_v = +\frac{250}{1 + 250(0{\cdot}026)} = 33$$ (plus sign to denote non-inverting amplifier)

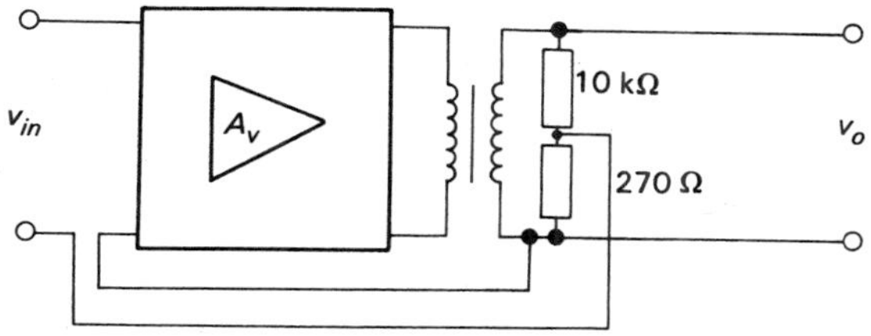

Figure 75 Negative feedback using a transformer

(*iii*) *Modification of the general feedback formula to show how connecting a load to an amplifying system affects the gain of the system*

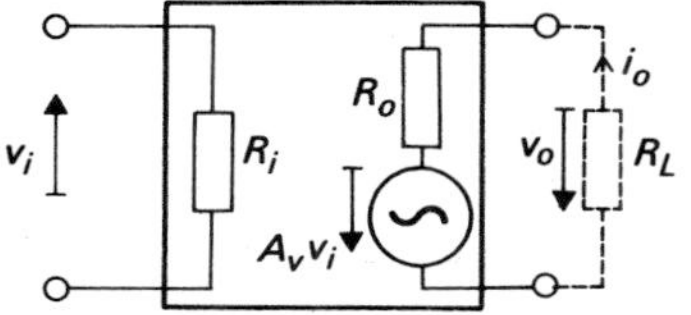

Figure 76 Equivalent circuit of an inverting amplifier

An amplifier system (with negative feedback) has both input and output impedance (resistance) and a voltage gain of A_v. A model of this is shown in Figure 76.

Let R_i = input impedance
R_0 = output impedance
R_L = load resistance

If no load resistance is connected, then $A_v v_i = v_0$ and no volt drop is measured across R_0.

When the load resistance R_L is connected, $i_0 = \dfrac{A_v v_i}{R_L + R_0}$ (8)

The new gain $A_v{}^1 = \dfrac{v_0}{v_1} = \dfrac{i_0 R_L}{v_i}$

Substituting equation 8 in 9 gives

$$A_v{}^1 = \left(\frac{A_v v_i}{R_L + R_0}\right) \times \frac{R_L}{v_i} = A_v \frac{R_L}{(R_L + R_0)}$$

Thus, the gain with the load connected is not the same as without the load connected. If negative feedback is applied to a system with a load resistor connected, then

$$G_v = \pm \frac{A_v{}^1}{1 + A_v{}^1 \beta}$$ (the sign is again dependent upon the type of amplifier used)

(*iv*) *Statement of the gain relationship for amplification stages connected in cascade*

When amplification stages are connected as shown in Figure 77, such that the output from one stage provides the input to the next, the overall gain of the system is given by

$$A_{vT} = A_{v1} \times A_{v2} \ldots \times A_{v2}$$

This is known as connecting stages in cascade.

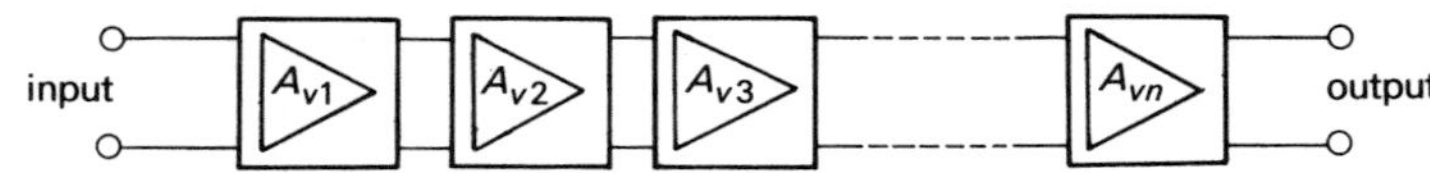

Figure 77 Gain of amplification system

(*v*) *Distinction between a.c. and d.c. negative feedback related to a series voltage feedback system*

Amplifier stages require d.c. supplies in order to operate correctly. The supplies need to be controlled and stabilized against external changes such as change in temperature. Now, d.c. negative feedback has no effect on the frequency response of the amplifier (which is controlled using a.c. negative feedback). Consider a series current negative feedback system as shown in Figure 78.

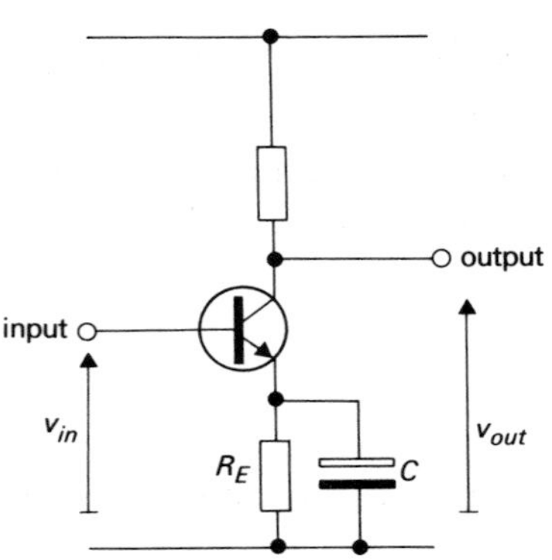

Figure 78 Diagram for d.c. and a.c. negative feedback

At very low frequencies, series current negative feedback is applied via the emitter resistor R_E. At this frequency the capacitor C behaves like an open circuit, and a high fraction of feedback is applied. The quiescent point or working point of the transistor is stabilized.

At mid-band frequencies the capacitor shorts out the emitter resistor and the gain of the amplifier is increased. The circuit is now connected as shown in Figure 79 such that two different forms of feedback are applied.

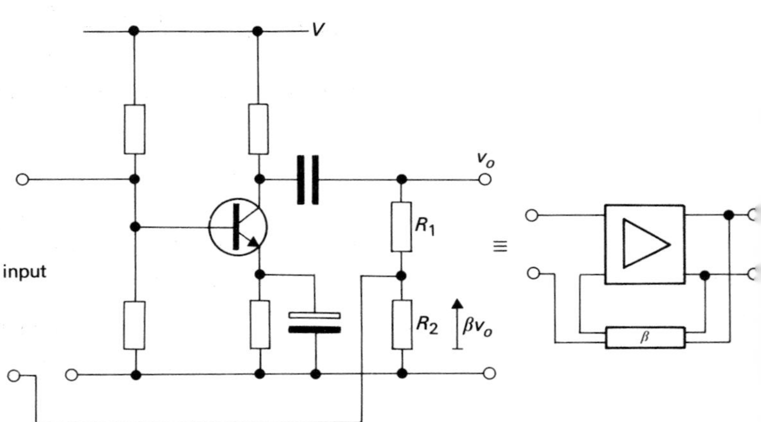

Figure 79 Circuit to combine both d.c. and a.c. negative feedback

The frequency response is controlled by the resistor chain R_1 and R_2 to give series voltage negative feedback, and the d.c. working point is controlled as previously described. One disadvantage of this circuit is that it is not possible to earth the feedback wire from the resistor network and the common transistor line. If the feedback wire is earthed the signal which is fed back is short circuited. The system could be used where the output is electrically isolated from the input by using a transformer (see Figure 80).

However if size is to be kept to a minimum and circuits are to be miniaturized, a transformer cannot be used. Other types of feedback circuits are used.

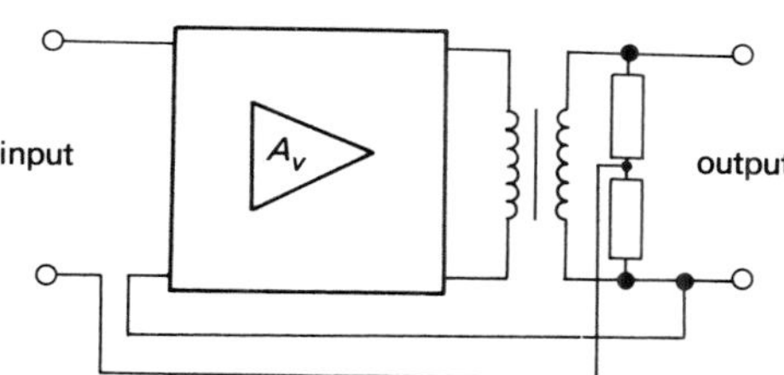

Figure 80 Series voltage negative feedback using a transformer

(*vi*) *Explanation of the practical operation of the emitter follower circuit*

As is shown in Figure 81, the output voltage is taken across the emitter resistor and is also fed back in series with the input. The bias current for the transistor is set by the value of R and a d.c. signal at the emitter is ensured under no signal (at the input) conditions.

The value of v_{BE} is small. Typical values are 0·2–0·7 volts, depending upon whether the transistor is made from germanium or silicon.

$$v_{in} = v_{BE} + v_{out}$$

Also, v_{BE} is small in comparison to v_{out} and hence $v_{in} \approx v_{out}$.

The output voltage follows the variations of the input voltage, and hence the name *emitter follower*. The circuit uses approximately 100% negative feedback and has the following characteristics

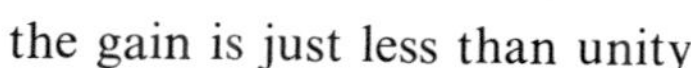

(i) the gain is just less than unity
(ii) the system is non-inverting
(iii) the input impedance is high
(iv) the output impedance is low
(v) the frequency response is good
(vi) the distortion content introduced is low
(vii) the input capacitance is low.

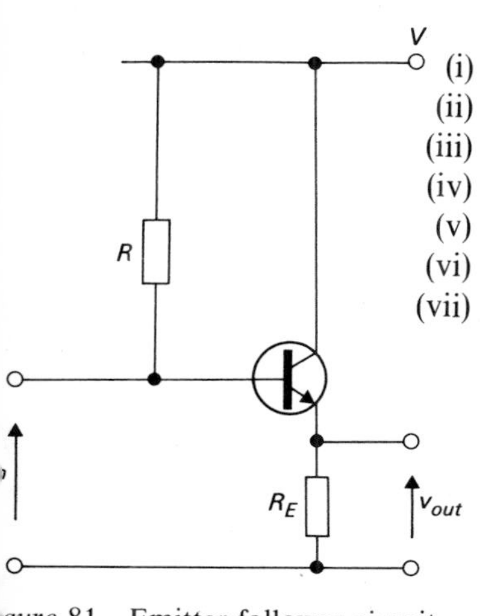

gure 81 Emitter follower circuit

The circuit of Figure 81 can be used to increase the input impedance of measuring devices when used as an input stage, or to match a high output impedance to a low impedance. A typical application of this occurs in logic applications as shown in Figure 82.

When logic circuits are interconnected, loading of stages takes place. If too many circuits are connected to the output of a logic stage, the voltage level drops to a value that is not high enough to energize the circuits which follow. Because the emitter follower has a lower output impedance than the logic circuit, it is able to supply more inputs to following stages without the voltage level falling to a 'non function' state. The technical term for this is to increase the 'fan-out' of the logic gate.

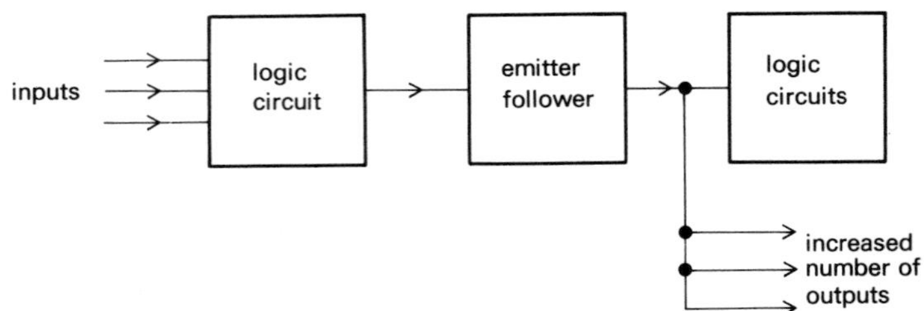

Figure 82 Practical application of an emitter follower circuit

(*vii*) *Summary of the overall stability of amplifiers using negative feedback containing up to three stages of amplification*

If the general feedback formula

$$G_v = \frac{A_v}{1 - A_v\beta}$$

is considered, what happens if the value of $A_v\beta$ approaches unity.

Then $G_v \rightarrow \frac{A_v}{0} \rightarrow \infty$

The amplifier is said to be *unstable*. For example if an amplifier system with a feedback fraction of $\frac{1}{50}$ is used at high frequencies, the gain could fall to 50, and $A_v\beta$ could equal unity.

For negative feedback

$$G_v = \pm \frac{A_v}{1 + A_v\beta}$$

At high frequencies, the positive sign in the denominator can become negative due to phase shift effects caused by the reactive components in the system.

For a single stage amplifier that is R–C coupled, the amount of phase shift required can never be reached at any frequency, because an R–C network can theoretically only cause 90° phase shift.

For a two stage amplifier the necessary phase shift could just occur but it is relatively simple to make the system stable.

For three or more stages, great care must be taken to prevent instability. Even if the amplifier is used over a restricted range the designer must ensure that it is stable at all frequencies from 0 to infinity.

(*viii*) *Summary of practical uses of different types of negative feedback connections*

The uses of series current and series voltage negative feedback have been described. Shunt voltage negative feedback is normally used with a high gain transistor, or with a number of stages connected in cascade. Shunt current negative feedback is seldom used. Hybrid negative feedback is generally used to provide a desired combination of features, as was shown in the sub-section (v).

Self-assessment questions

7 Give two reasons why the gain of an amplifier may change under normal operating conditions when no negative feedback is applied.

8 Delete the incorrect word in each of the following statements.
The application of negative feedback results:

(i) in the effective gain being increased/reduced and stabilized/de-stabilized

(ii) in the distortion being increased/reduced, and therefore in better/poorer quality output

(iii) in the bandwidth being increased/reduced.

9 Indicate in the column provided in Table 8 which of the following items describe how the impedances (resistances) vary as the type of negative feedback is varied.

type of negative feedback	impedances input	output
A series voltage	1 increases	increases
B shunt voltage	2 increases	decreases
C series current	3 decreases	decreases
D shunt current	4 decreases	increases

A	
B	
C	
D	

Table 8

10 What is the feedback fraction developed across R_2 for two resistors R_1 and R_2 of a potential divider chain? The resistance of R_1 is 25 kΩ and the resistance of R_2 is 1 kΩ.

11 A non-inverting amplifier stage has a gain of 30 with a negativ feedback loop connected. When the loop is removed the gain of th stage is 300. Calculate the feedback fraction.

12 The amplifier stage used in Question 11 has an output resistance o 500 Ω. If a load resistor of 10 000 Ω is connected, calculate the gain o the stage with the negative feedback loop connected.

13 Two amplifier stages are connected in cascade. They have stage gain of 50 and 20 respectively.

(*a*) The gain of the overall system = 70
(*b*) The gain of the overall system = 30
(*c*) The gain of the overall system = 100
(*d*) The gain of the overall system = 1000

Select the correct response.

14 Complete the following sentences by deleting the incorrect words.
A.c./d.c. negative feedback is used to control the frequency respons of an amplifier. D.c. negative feedback has no/much control o amplifier frequency response, but has no/much control over th working point of the amplifier.

15 Complete the following sentences, which relate to a negative feedbac system, by deleting the incorrect words.
When the whole of the output voltage is fed back in series with th input, then series/shunt voltage/current negative feedback is applied This form of negative feedback is used in the common emitter/collec tor circuit.

16 Underline the correct alternative.

(*a*) Hybrid negative feedback is generally used to provide a desire combination of features as required for a particular circuit.
TRUE/FALSI

(*b*) A single stage amplifier that is *R–C* coupled and has negativ feedback applied can become unstable at high frequencies.
TRUE/FALSI

17 Underline the correct alternatives.
If negative feedback is applied to an amplifier stage it causes:

(*a*) the gain to: increase, decrease, remain unchanged
(*b*) the bandwidth to: increase, decrease, remain unchanged
(*c*) distortion to: increase, decrease, remain unchanged
(*d*) gain stability to: increase, decrease, remain unchanged
(*e*) noise to: increase, decrease, remain unchanged.

18 Complete the following sentences by deleting the incorrect words.

(*a*) The emitter follower circuit uses 100 per cent series/shunt voltage/current negative feedback.

(*b*) In a common emitter amplifier the emitter resistor applied series/shunt voltage/current negative feedback.

19 Underline the correct alternatives.
The common emitter circuit has

(*a*) input impedance which is: low, high
(*b*) output impedance which is: low, high
(*c*) output voltage which is: inverted, non-inverted
(*d*) noise content at the output which is: low, high
(*e*) frequency response which is: good, poor
(*f*) gain which is: greater than unity, less than unity.

20 An inverting amplifier has a gain of 10 and a feedback fraction (using a resistor network) of 0·09, which is used to apply negative feedback. Calculate the loop gain and the closed loop gain.

21 In an amplifier with a constant input of 1 V, the output falls from 50 V to 25 V when negative feedback is applied. Calculate the feedback fraction. If, due to a change in external parameters, the amplifier gain falls to 40, find the percentage reduction in stage gain

(i) without negative feedback connected
(ii) with negative feedback connected.

22 An inverting amplifier has a voltage gain of 48 dB at 5 kHz, 60 dB at 500 kHz, and 54 dB at 5 MHz. Negative feedback (using a resistor network) reduces the gain at 500 kHz to 40 dB. If the feedback fraction is unaltered by change of frequency, find the new gain at 5 kHz and 5 MHz.

Solutions to self-assessment questions (pages 93–95)

7 The gain may change because of
(*a*) changes in supply voltage
(*b*) changes in temperature
(*c*) changes in environmental conditions.

8 The correct statements are:
(i) in the effective gain being reduced and stabilized
(ii) in the distortion being reduced and therefore in better quality output
(iii) in the bandwidth being increased.

9

A	2
B	3
C	1
D	4

10 $\beta = \frac{R_2}{R_1 + R_2} = \frac{1000}{25\,000 + 1000} = \frac{1}{26}$

11 $G_v = \pm \frac{A_v}{1 + A_v\beta}$

$\therefore +30 = +\frac{300}{1 + 300\beta}$

$\therefore 1 + 300\beta = \frac{300}{30}$

$\therefore 300\beta = 9$

$\therefore \beta = \frac{3}{100}$

12 $A_v{}^1 = \frac{A_v R_L}{R_L + R_0}$

$= 300\frac{10\,000}{(10\,000 + 500)} = 286$

$\therefore G_v = \frac{286}{1 + 286(\frac{3}{100})} = 29{\cdot}85$

Without negative feedback the gain falls from 300 to 286.
With negative feedback the gain hardly changes.

13 (*d*) 1000

14 The correct sentences are:
A.c. negative feedback is used to control the frequency response of an amplifier.
D.c. negative feedback has no control on amplifier frequency response but has much control over the working point of the amplifier.

15 The correct sentences are:
When the whole of the output voltage is fed back in series with the input, then series voltage negative feedback is applied. This form of negative feedback is used in the common emitter circuit.

16
(*a*) TRUE
(*b*) FALSE, because the maximum phase shift can only be 90°.

17 The correct alternatives are
(*a*) decreases
(*b*) increases
(*c*) decreases
(*d*) increases
(*e*) decreases.

18 The sentences are correct when written as follows:
(*a*) The emitter follower circuit uses 100 per cent series voltage negative feedback.
(*b*) In a common emitter amplifier the emitter resistor applies series current negative feedback.

19 The correct alternatives are:
(*a*) high
(*b*) low
(*c*) non-inverted
(*d*) low
(*e*) good
(*f*) less than unity.

20 Loop gain $= A_v\beta = 10 \times 0{\cdot}09 = 0{\cdot}9$

closed loop gain $G_v = -\frac{A_v}{1 + A_v\beta}$

$= -\frac{10}{1 + 0{\cdot}9} = -5{\cdot}3$

21 For an amplifier $G_v = \pm\frac{A_v}{1 + A_v\beta}$

Assuming an inverting amplifier or a non-inverting amplifier

$$-25 = -\frac{50}{1 + 50\beta}$$

or $$25 = \frac{50}{1 + 50\beta}$$

$\therefore 1 + 50\beta = 2$ for both systems

$\therefore \beta = \frac{1}{50}$

If A_v reduces to 40

percentage fall in gain

$= \left(\frac{50 - 40}{50}\right) \times 100\%$

$= 20\%$ without negative feedback

Also $G_v = \frac{40}{1 + 40(\frac{1}{50})} = 22{\cdot}2$ with negative feedback

$\therefore$ percentage fall in gain

$= \left(\frac{25 - 22{\cdot}2}{25}\right) \times 100\%$

$= 11{\cdot}2\%$ with negative feedback

22 At 500 kHz $40 = 20 \log_{10} G_v$ and

$60 = 20 \log_{10} A_v$

$\therefore G_v = 100$

$\therefore A_v = 1000$

$\therefore -100 = \frac{-1000}{1 + 1000\beta}$

$\therefore \beta = \frac{9}{1000}$

At 5 kHz $48 = 20 \log_{10} A_v$

$A_v = 251{\cdot}2$

$G_v = -\frac{251{\cdot}2}{1 + (251{\cdot}2)(\frac{9}{1000})}$

$\therefore G_v = -77$

At 5 MHz $54 = 20 \log_{10} A_v$

$A_v = 501{\cdot}2$

$G_v = -\frac{501{\cdot}2}{1 + (501{\cdot}2)(\frac{9}{1000})}$

$\therefore G_v = -91$

Topic area Simple resistive capacitive networks

After reading the following material, the reader shall:

7 Understand the operation of pulse shaping circuits.

7.1 Explain the response of a resistor and a capacitor connected in series:

(*a*) when the capacitor is initially uncharged and the series circuit is connected to a supply voltage V_s

(*b*) when the capacitor is initially charged and then discharged through the resistor.

7.2 State the practical importance of five time constants for the series *CR* circuit.

7.3 Sketch and label a rectangular pulse-wave form showing pulse width, pulse amplitude, rise-time and decay-time.

Many of the pulse shaping circuits used in electrical and electronic circuits (like the time base circuit of the oscilloscope) are based upon the *CR* network, e.g. the differentiating circuit and the integrating circuit. To understand how these circuits work, it is necessary to examine in some detail the charging and discharging process of the *CR* circuit.

A series *CR* circuit is shown in Figure 83, where the switch is set to position 2 and the capacitor is discharged. At the instant of time when the switch is changed to position 1 ($t=0$), and for all values of t afterwards, the voltage applied to A and B must be equal to the sum of the voltage across the capacitor (v_c) and the voltage across the resistor (v_R). The mathematical expression for this statement is

$$V_s = v_c + v_R \qquad (1)$$

where v_c is the instantaneous voltage across C

v_R is the instantaneous voltage across R

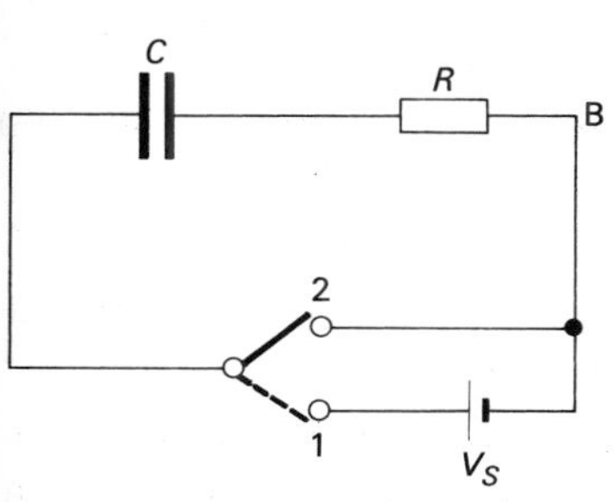

Figure 83 The series *CR* circuit

If these voltages are measured in the laboratory and a graph plotted of voltage against time, they are found to vary exponentially, as shown in Figure 84. The maximum value of current flows (in direction A to B on Figure 83) at $t=0$ to charge up the capacitor. Thus the voltage across the capacitor starts at zero and rises to a final value of V_s.

For equation 1 to be true, the voltage across the resistor must initially be V_s and fall to a final value of zero, such that at all instants of time the sum of v_c and v_R must be equal to V_s.

A further investigation of equation 1 shows that the followin expressions are true (the procedure to obtain these expressions i beyond the level set by the objectives but they are important enoug for the reader to know of them at this stage):

$$v_c = V_S(1 - e^{-t/CR})$$
$$v_R = V_S e^{-t/CR}$$

At time $t=0$ substituting in the value of t gives:

$$v_c = V_S(1 - e^{-0}) \qquad \text{and } v_R = V_S e^{-0} \quad (e^{-0} = 1)$$
$$\therefore v_c = V_S(1-1) \qquad \therefore v_R = V_S$$
$$\therefore v_c = 0$$

Both these results agree with the practical measurement.

At a time when t is very large, say $t = \infty$, substituting in the value o t gives:

$$v_c = V_S(1 - e^{-\infty}) \qquad \text{and } v_R = V_S e^{-\infty} \quad (e^{-\infty} = 0)$$
$$\therefore v_c = V_S \qquad v_R = 0$$

Both these results agree with the practical measurement. Values of between 0 and ∞ can be measured or estimated, and hence values of and v_R found. These verify the curves of Figure 84 completely.

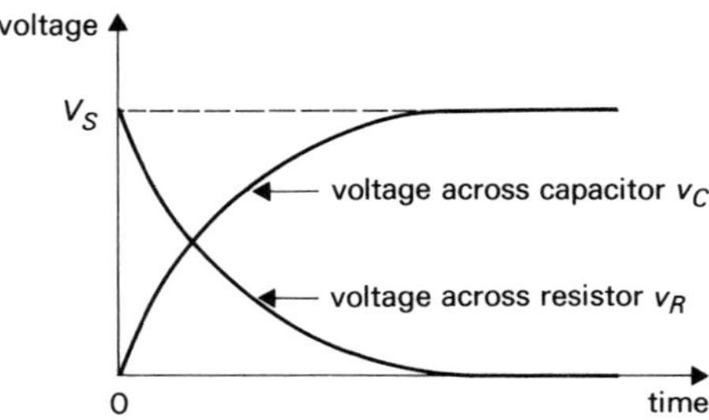

Figure 84 Graphical display of v_c and v_R

It should be noted that the final values are reached theoretically onl after an infinite time. The circuit is then said to have reached *stead state conditions*. In practice, a good approximation is to assume tha final values are reached if the voltage across the capacitor reaches 1% of the applied voltage. (The reason for this is explained later.)

Assume now that the circuit has reached steady state conditions an the switch is then moved to position 2 in Figure 83.

The capacitor becomes the source of energy and discharges via th resistor R. The current flows in the *opposite* direction to the chargin direction. The voltage measured across the resistor must now *chang in polarity* because the current direction through it has reversed. Consider the voltage waveforms measured in the complete switching cycle shown in Figure 85.

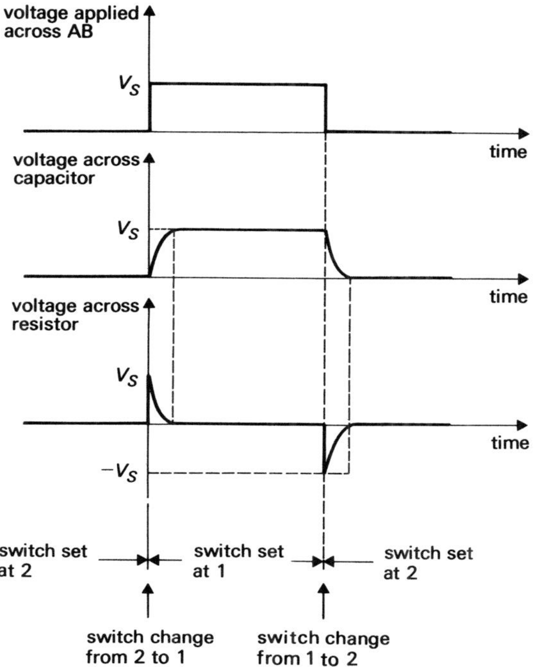

Figure 85 Voltage waveforms for the *C R* circuit

If the switching cycle is repeated the voltage applied across AB becomes a rectangular waveform, and the voltages across the capacitor and the resistor repeat the shape shown in Figure 85.

The circuit of Figure 83 is redrawn in Figure 86. In Figure 86(*b*) the supply has been removed and the terminals AB have been redrawn. In Figure 86(*c*) the resistor has been repositioned such that the voltage measured across it is called the output. In Figure 86(*d*) the capacitor has been repositioned such that the voltage measured across it is called the output.

It can be seen that the circuit has in no way changed from the original circuit under charge and discharge conditions, and the output waveform sketch is the same as that shown in Figure 85.

Another way of representing the conditions of Figure 83 is with a rectangular waveshape input as shown in Figure 87 for the circuits shown in Figure 86(*c*) and 86(*d*).

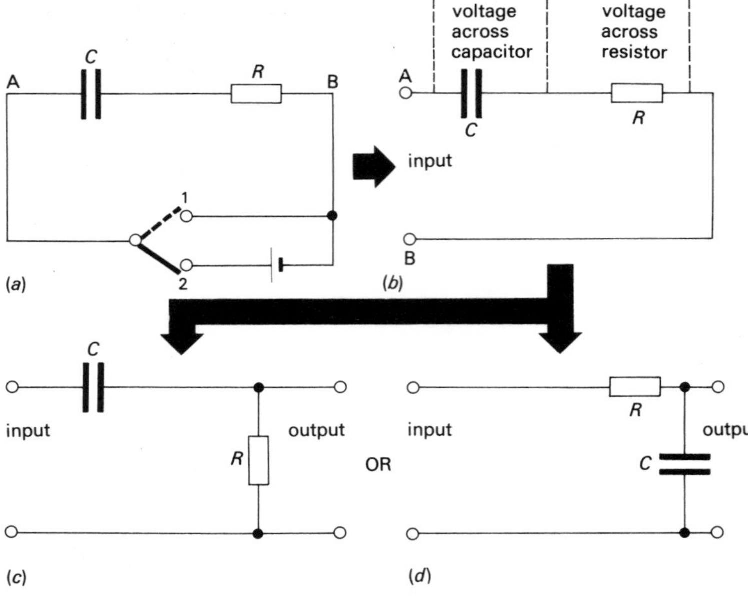

Figure 86 Reconstruction of *C R* circuit

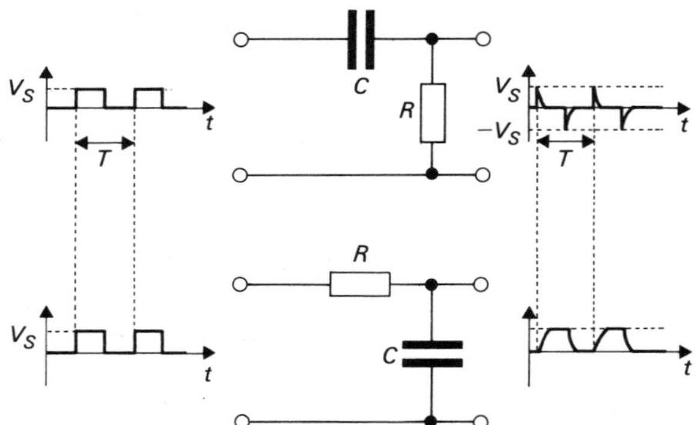

Figure 87 Response of *C R* circuits to a rectangular waveshape

What happens to the output waveforms if T becomes smaller but the values of C and R remain the same? Consider the different cases shown in Figure 88. In each case the voltage across the resistor and the voltage across the capacitor is shown. The waveforms for the final case do not reach the maximum value. In fact the pulse time T is too short to allow this to happen. Consider the diagram shown in Figure 89.

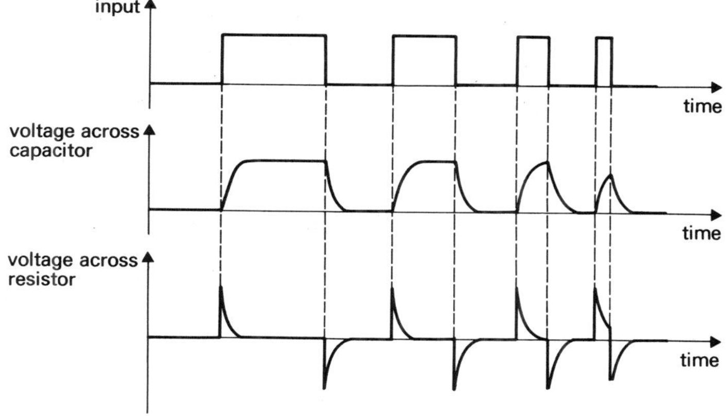

Figure 88 Effect of decreasing t

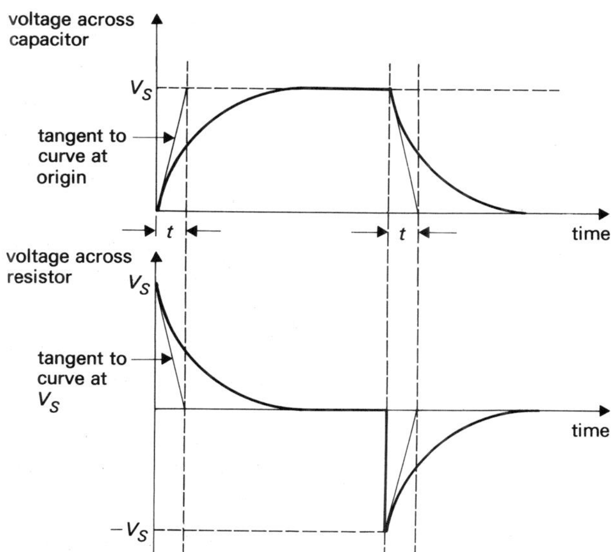

Figure 89 Time constant of a CR circuit

From the diagram it is found that in all cases if the change of voltage continues at its *initial rate*, the final value is reached in t seconds. This is true for any series CR circuit, and it is so important that the time taken is called the *time constant* of the series CR circuit.

The time constant for a series CR circuit is the time taken (measured in seconds) to reach the steady state value, if the change continues at its initial rate.

In the diagram it can be seen that the initial value is either zero or v_S and the final value is either v_S or zero, depending on whether the capacitor charges or discharges. This is for a voltage waveform. In fact a similar result can be shown to be true, for a current waveform (or a charge waveform) analysis of this type of circuit. The time constant for the CR network is given by

$t = CR$ where t = time constant in seconds
C = value of capacitance in farads
R = value of resistance in ohms

Another important result is that in practice steady state conditions can be assumed to have been reached (to within 1 per cent of the final value) after a time equivalent to five time constants;
i.e. steady state conditions are reached in $5 \times CR$ seconds

This means in practice that after 5 CR seconds there is an immediate knowledge of when a completed change has taken place. For example in Figure 87, providing T is greater than five time constants (i.e. $T > 5\,CR$), the effect of the CR network on the pulse wave can be easily estimated. As T becomes less than 5 CR then the waveshape changes and further investigation is required.

In practice it is impossible to change from one voltage level to another instantaneously. Thus a change from zero to V volts takes a finite time. In a rectangular wave form generator, this finite time is made as small as possible to try and produce the theoretical waveshape shown in Figure 90.

The wave shape produced across the capacitor in the series RC network is as shown in Figure 90, and practical estimates of the rise time and decay time are obtained as follows.

The time taken for the waveshape to rise from 10 per cent of the steady state value to 90 per cent of the steady state value is called the *rise time*.

The time taken for the waveshape to fall from 90 per cent of the steady state value to 10 per cent of the steady state value is called the *decay time*.

It can be shown that for a series CR circuit

rise time = decay time = $2{\cdot}2\ CR$

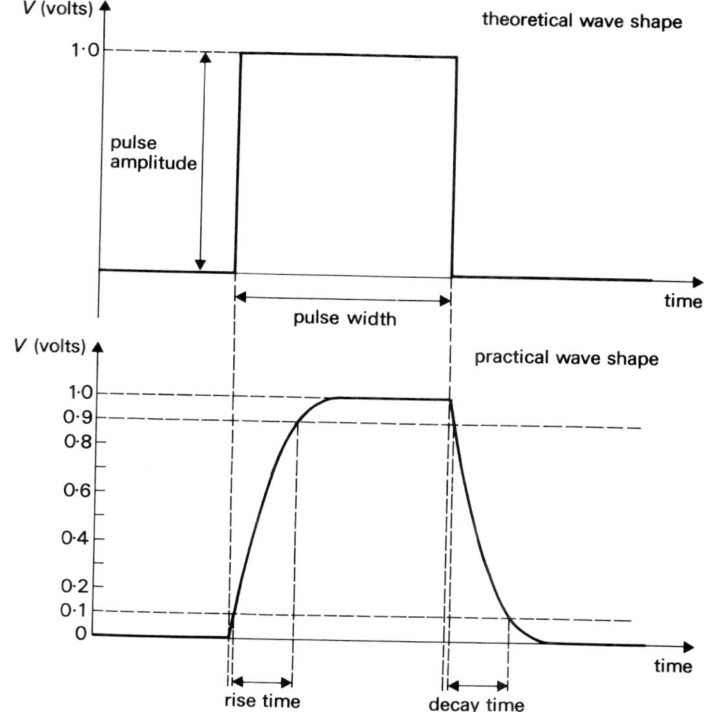

Figure 90 Theoretical and practical pulse waveshape

Self-assessment questions

1 Consider the circuit diagram shown in Figure 83.
Stage 1: The switch is initially at position 2. The next statements follow in sequence, assuming initially steady state conditions exist.

(*a*) The voltage across the capacitor is zero.

TRUE/FALSE

(*b*) The voltage across the resistor is V_S volts.

TRUE/FALSE

Stage 2: The switch is changed to position 1.

(*c*) A current flows in the direction AB

TRUE/FALSE

(*d*) The capacitor begins to charge up

TRUE/FALSE

(*e*) The initial voltage across the resistor is V_S volts

TRUE/FALSE

(*f*) The final voltage across the capacitor is V_S volts

TRUE/FALSE

Steady state conditions are reached.
Stage 3: The switch is changed to position 2.

(*g*) The voltage across the capacitor is always larger than the voltage across the resistor

TRUE/FALSE

(*h*) A current flows in direction AB

TRUE/FALSE

(*i*) While current flows, the potential drop across the resistor is of opposite polarity to the voltage across the resistor during stage 2

TRUE/FALSE

(*j*) The voltage across the capacitor is always equal to the voltage across the resistor

TRUE/FALSE

2 Sketch the voltage waveforms occurring across the capacitor and the resistor for each of the three stages of Question 1.

3 Complete the following sentences by adding the correct word (or words). The sentences relate to the series *CR* network.

(i) The time constant for a series *CR* circuit is the time taken to reach the ____________ ____________ value, if the change continues at its initial rate.

(ii) The time constant $t = CR$, where C = value of capacitance in farads and R = value of resistance in ohms: t is measured in ____________.

(iii) In practice, steady state conditions can be assumed to have been reached after ____________ time constants.

(iv) The time taken for the waveshape to rise from 10 per cent of the steady state value to 90 per cent of the steady state value is called the ____________ ____________.

(v) The time taken for the waveshape to fall from 90 per cent of the steady state value to 10 per cent of the steady state value is called the ____________ ____________.

4 The time taken for a pulse waveshape to rise from 10 per cent of the steady state value to 90 per cent of the steady state value is 5 *CR*.

TRUE/FALSE

5 Sketch and label a rectangular pulse waveform showing pulse width, pulse amplitude, rise time and decay time.

After reading the following material, the reader shall:

7.4 Sketch the circuit diagram of an integrating circuit.

7.5 Sketch the output waveform of an integrating circuit when a rectangular pulse is applied to the input such that:

(*a*) the pulse width is much longer than the *CR* time

(*b*) the pulse width equals five time constants

(*c*) the pulse width is much shorter than the *CR* time.

7.6 Sketch the circuit diagram of a differentiating circuit.

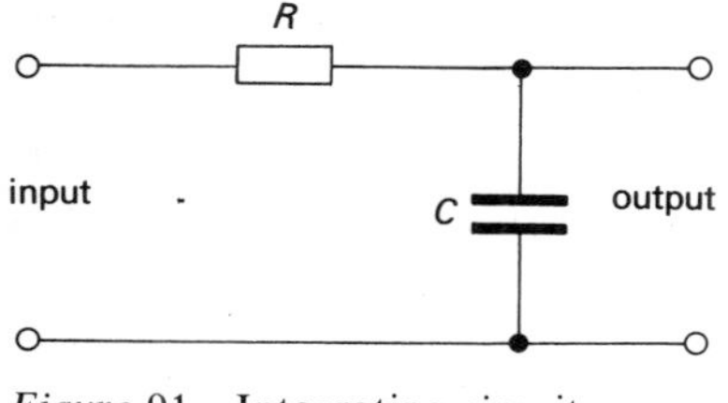

Figure 91 Integrating circuit

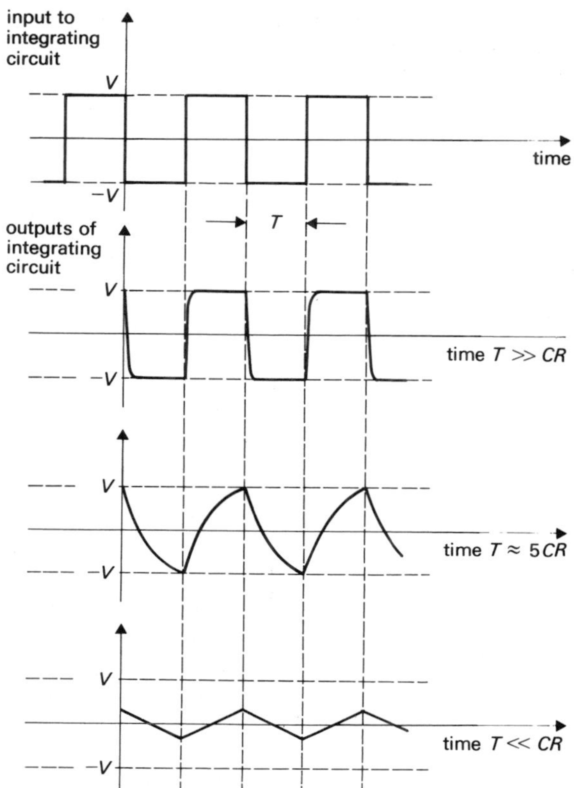

Figure 92 Response of an integrating circuit to a continuous rectangular pulse waveshape for different time constants

7.7 Sketch the output waveform of a differentiating circuit when a rectangular input pulse is applied to the input such that:

(*a*) the pulse width is much longer than the CR time

(*b*) the pulse width equals five time constants

(*c*) the pulse width is much shorter than the CR time.

7.8 Give examples of the use of a differentiating circuit and an integrating circuit.

The series RC circuit has been re-arranged in the form shown in Figure 91, such that the voltage across the capacitor is made the output. If a pulse waveform is applied at the input the shape of the output waveform depends on the values of C and R.

When the capacitance and resistance are varied and the pulse width is kept constant, the time constant of the circuit varies as is shown in Figure 92.

Solutions to self-assessment questions (pages 103–104)

1
(a) TRUE
(b) FALSE
(c) TRUE
(d) TRUE
(e) TRUE
(f) TRUE
(g) FALSE
(h) FALSE
(i) TRUE
(j) FALSE

2 See Figure 85.

3
(i) steady state
(ii) seconds
(iii) five
(iv) rise time
(v) decay time.

4 FALSE

5 See Figure 90.

For a time constant small compared with the pulse width, the output waveform easily reaches the final value after the initial change.

When the pulse width is equal to five time constants, the output waveform just reaches its final value. The output waveshape is curved on both the rise and decay parts of the waveform.

For a very large time constant, the output waveshape can neither rise to its final value nor decay to its final value before the input pulse changes levels, to give the waveshape shown in the diagram of Figure 92.

The circuit behaves differently according to the relation between time constant and pulse width.

Note: For a small time constant compared to a large pulse width, the *CR* circuit is called a *coupling circuit*. For a large time constant compared to a small pulse width, the *CR* circuit is called an *integrating circuit*.

The series *CR* circuit has been re-arranged in the form shown in Figure 93, such that the voltage across the resistor is made the output. If a pulse waveform is applied at the input, the shape of the output waveform depends on the values of *C* and *R*. When the capacitance and resistance are varied, and the pulse width is kept constant, the time constant of the circuit varies as is shown in Figure 94.

For a small time constant compared with the pulse width, the output waveform easily reaches the final value after the initial change. When the pulse width is equal to five time constants, the output waveform just reaches its final value. The output waveshape is less 'spikey' as shown in the diagram. For a very large time constant, the output waveshape can neither decay to its final value nor rise to its final value before the input pulse changes levels, to give the waveshape shown in the diagram of Figure 94.

The circuit behaves differently according to the relation between time constant and pulse width.

Note: For a small time constant compared to large pulse width, the circuit is called a *differentiating circuit*. For a large time constant compared to a small pulse width the circuit is called a *coupling circuit*.

Thus, the *CR* circuit can be used for waveshaping. By careful choice of the values of *C* and *R* the differentiating circuit can be made to have no effect on the pulse wave as it passes through (the coupling circuit), or the wave can be converted to a series of spikes that may be used as trigger pulses. Similarly the integrating circuit can be made to have no effect on the pulse wave as it passes through (the coupling circuit), or the wave can be converted to a triangular waveshape.

The two circuits can also be made to perform the mathematical functions of differentiation and integration.

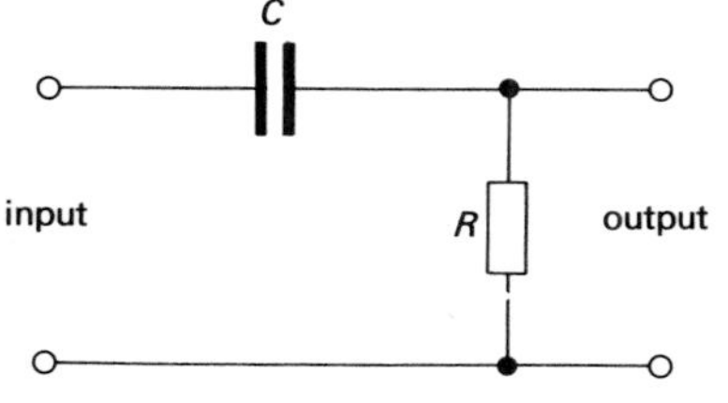

Figure 93 Differentiating circuit

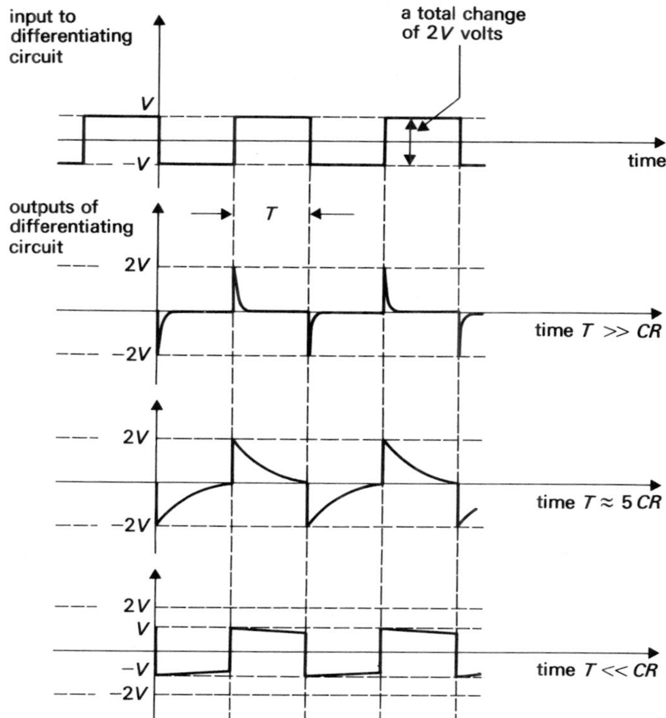

Figure 94 Response of a differentiating circuit to a continuous rectangular pulse waveshape for different time constants

Consider the ideal case where the voltage level changes instantaneously from zero to V volts, as shown in Figure 95. This part of the rectangular waveform is often called a *step function.* If a step function is applied as the input to an integrating circuit, the theoretical output is as shown in Figure 95. In practice this response is not obtained; the actual result is shown for the purposes of comparison in Figure 95.

From the graph, the ideal and actual responses are alike only for the initial rise part of the curve or for

$$v_{out} \ll v_{in}$$

In practice, for $t + 0{\cdot}1\ CR$ the difference in value between the ideal and practical cases is approximately 5 per cent (see Figure 95).

Thus a series CR circuit can function as a mathematical integrator only if v_{out} is restricted to values significantly less than v_{in}. This means the signal attenuation necessary to achieve mathematical accuracy of integration results in output voltages which are too small for practical use.

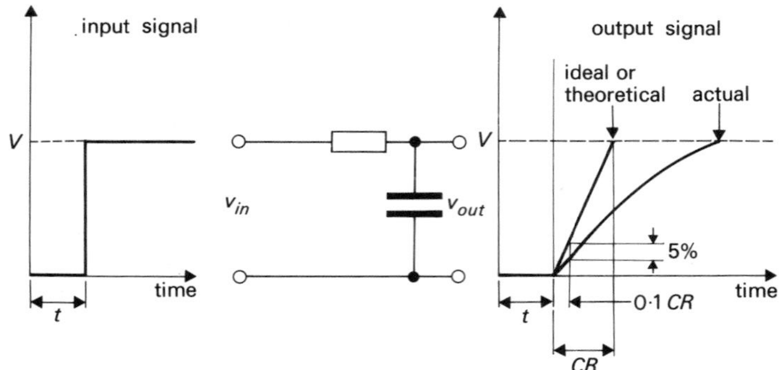

Figure 95 Input and output of an integrating circuit

For this reason the *CR* circuit is not used for mathematical integration. However the mathematical integrating circuit is the basis of the analogue computer. This circuit function is provided by using an operational amplifier with a capacitor as the feedback component. The attenuation problem of the *CR* network is then avoided (for further details see topic area Integrated circuits).

Consider the case where the voltage increases uniformly from zero to a fixed value. This part of a sawtooth waveform is known as a *ramp function*. If a ramp function is applied as the input to a differentiating circuit, the theoretical output is as shown in Figure 96. In practice the ideal response is not obtained; the actual result is shown for the purposes of comparison in Figure 96.

From the graph, there is an initial error in the output. It can be reduced by making the time constant small. Thus the value of *R* or *C* is made smaller. This means the output voltage is reduced, so that increased accuracy is realized at the price of attenuation of input signal.

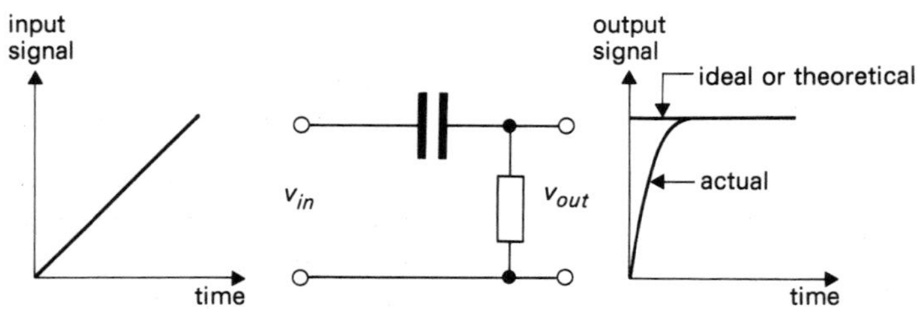

Figure 96 Input and output of a differentiating circuit

In practice the *CR* circuit is not used for mathematical differentiation because:

(i) noise contains higher frequencies than those to be differentiated; hence differentiation accentuates noise

(ii) if the differentiation of a discontinuous function is involved the circuit can provide only an approximation.

Thus the *CR* circuits are used mainly for *curve shaping* or *pulse shaping.*

The integrating circuit can be used to provide the waveshape required for the time base of an oscilloscope. As shown in Figure 97, the mark to space ratio of the rectangular pulse is arranged to give a short flyback time.

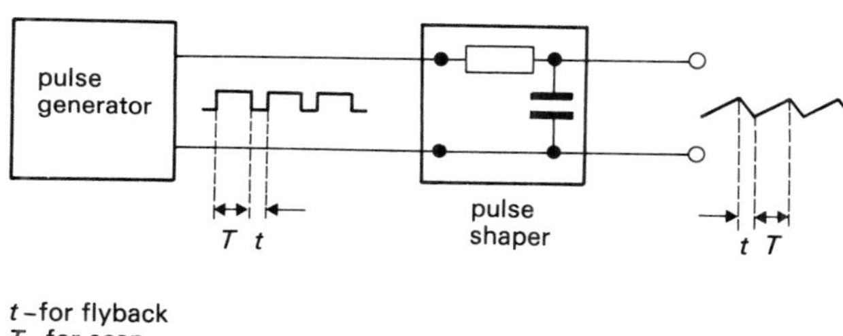

Figure 97 Practical use of the integrating circuit

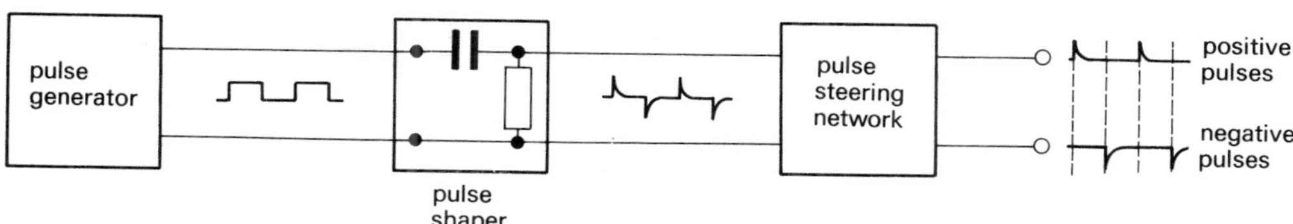

Figure 98 Practical use of the differentiating circuit

The differentiating circuit can be used to provide either positive- or negative-going pulses as shown in Figure 98. These pulses can be used to synchronize multivibrators. Alternatively they can be used to introduce a time delay, i.e. the leading edge of the rectangular pulse is delayed by using the negative pulse produced by the trailing edge of the same rectangular pulse. For more details see topic area Oscillators.

Self-assessment questions

6 Sketch the diagram of
(*a*) an integrating circuit
(*b*) a differentiating circuit.

7 For each of the three cases shown in Figure 99, sketch the output waveforms for the integrating circuit and the differentiating circuit.

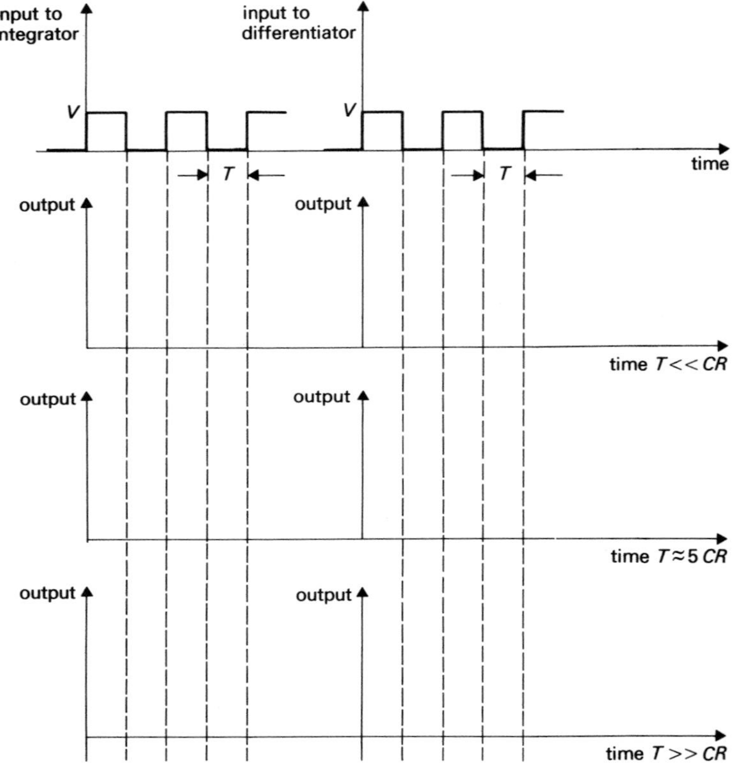

Figure 99 Waveshape for Self-assessment question 7

8 State the main limitation of the circuits of Question 6 when used to provide mathematical functions.

9 State one practical use of
(*a*) an integrating circuit
(*b*) a differentiating circuit.

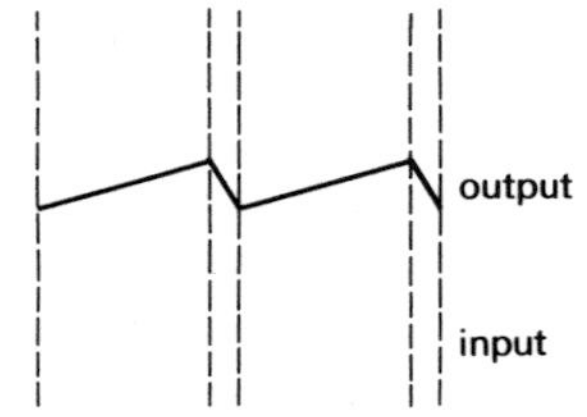

Figure 100 Waveshape for Self-assessment question 10

10 In Figure 100, the voltage waveform shown is the output from an integrating circuit. Sketch below it the input voltage waveform.

11 In Figure 101, label the block whose function is indicated by the input and output waveforms.

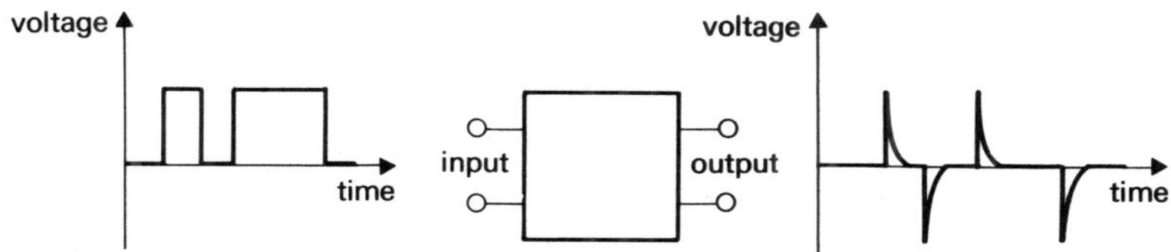

Figure 101 Diagram for Self-assessment question 11

12 Which of the outputs shown in Figure 102 is obtained when a 10 kHz square wave is applied to a differentiating circuit?

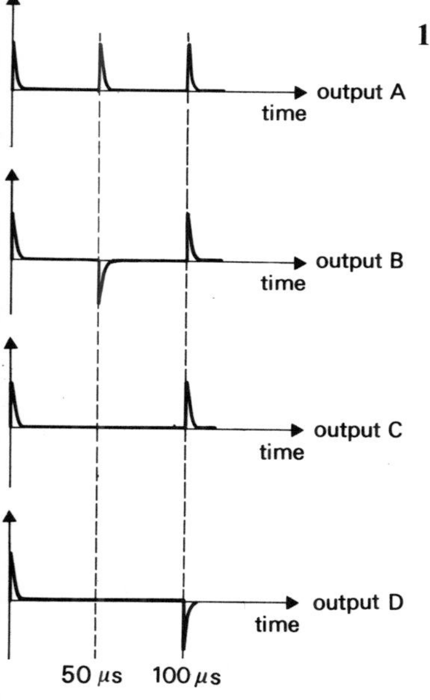

Figure 102 Diagram for Self-assessment question 12

13 A pulse waveform similar to that shown in Figure 103 is applied to an integrating circuit and then to a differentiating circuit. Which output (A, B, C or D) is obtained from an integrating circuit? Which output (A, B, C or D) is obtained from a differentiating circuit?

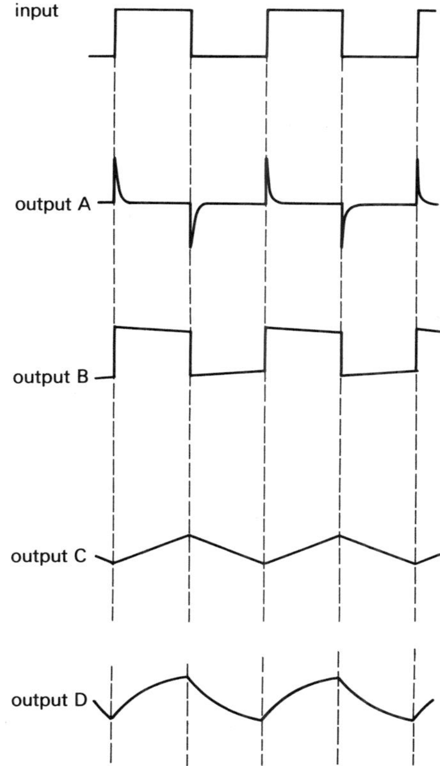

Figure 103 Waveshapes for Self-assessment question 13

Underline the correct word in Questions 14 and 15.

14 When an integrating circuit has a time constant that is much greater than the pulse width of the applied input signal, it behaves as an integrator.

TRUE/FALSE

15 When a differentiating circuit has a time constant that is much greater than the pulse width of the applied input signal, it behaves as a differentiator.

TRUE/FALSE

Topic area Oscillators

After reading the following material, the reader shall:

8 Describe the characteristics of basic sinusoidal oscillator circuits.
8.1 State that oscillations can be produced by an amplifier with positive feedback.
8.2 Describe the conditions required such that maintained oscillations can be produced by an amplifier with feedback.
8.3 Explain the operation of
(*a*) *LC* tuned oscillator
(*b*) *RC* oscillator.
8.4 State the factors that affect short term and long term frequency stability of oscillators.
8.5 Describe methods of improving the frequency stability of oscillators, e.g. piezoelectric crystal control.
8.6 Explain the practical operation of a single stage transistor oscillator using a crystal in the frequency determining unit.

Purpose of an oscillator

The purpose of an oscillator is to produce an output signal that:
(i) changes magnitudes between stated levels
(ii) produces a recurring waveshape at the required frequency.

The frequency and the waveshape chosen for oscillation depend mainly on the application for which the output signal is required.

Consider the diagram shown in Figure 107. If a pulse of energy is applied to the frequency determining unit, the unit oscillates, but due to practical considerations this natural oscillation always dies down to zero. There are always *associated losses* in this part. If sufficient energy is applied to the oscillatory unit to overcome these losses, and if it is applied at an appropriate time in the cycle, oscillations continue indefinitely to provide a *maintained oscillatory unit*, shown in Figure 108.

This addition of energy is provided by the loss replacement unit.

Solutions to self-assessment questions (pages 110–112)

6 See Figure 104.

7 The output waveforms are shown in Figure 105.

8 The signal attenuation necessary to achieve accuracy of integration or differentiation results in output voltages which are too small for practical use.

9

(*a*) The integrating circuit can be used to provide the waveshape required for the time base of an oscilloscope.

(*b*) The differentiating circuit can be used to provide trigger pulses, and to produce time delays.

10 Both output and input waveforms are shown in Figure 106.

11 Differentiating circuit.

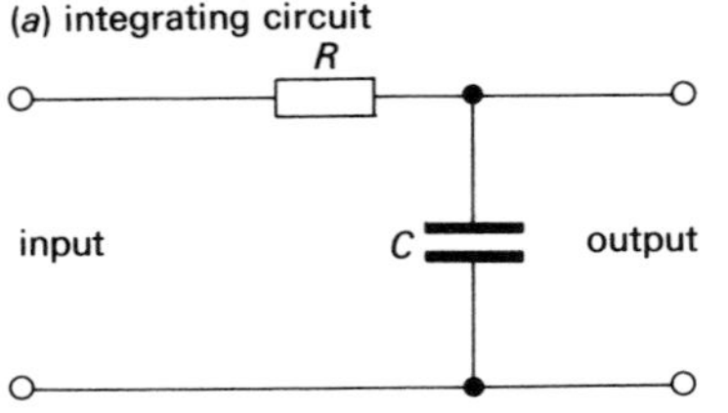

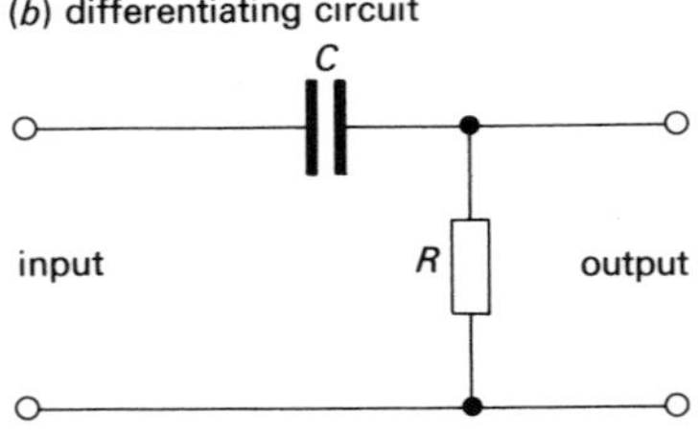

Figure 104 Solution to Self-assessment question 6

12 Output D.

13 Integrating circuit — output C. Differentiating circuit — output A

14 TRUE.

15 FALSE. When a differentiating circuit has a time constant that is much less than the pulse width of the applied input signal, it behaves as a differentiator. For a large time constant it behaves as a coupling circuit.

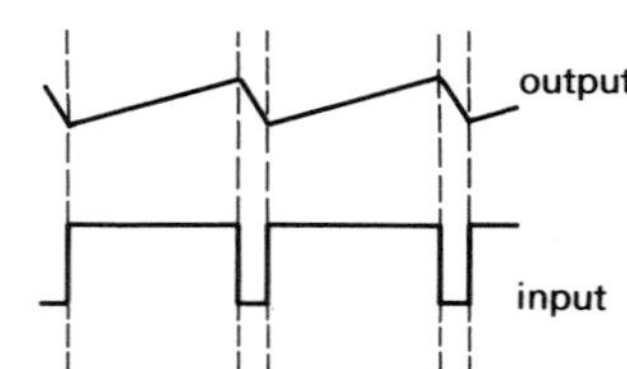

Figure 106 Solution to Self-assessment question 10

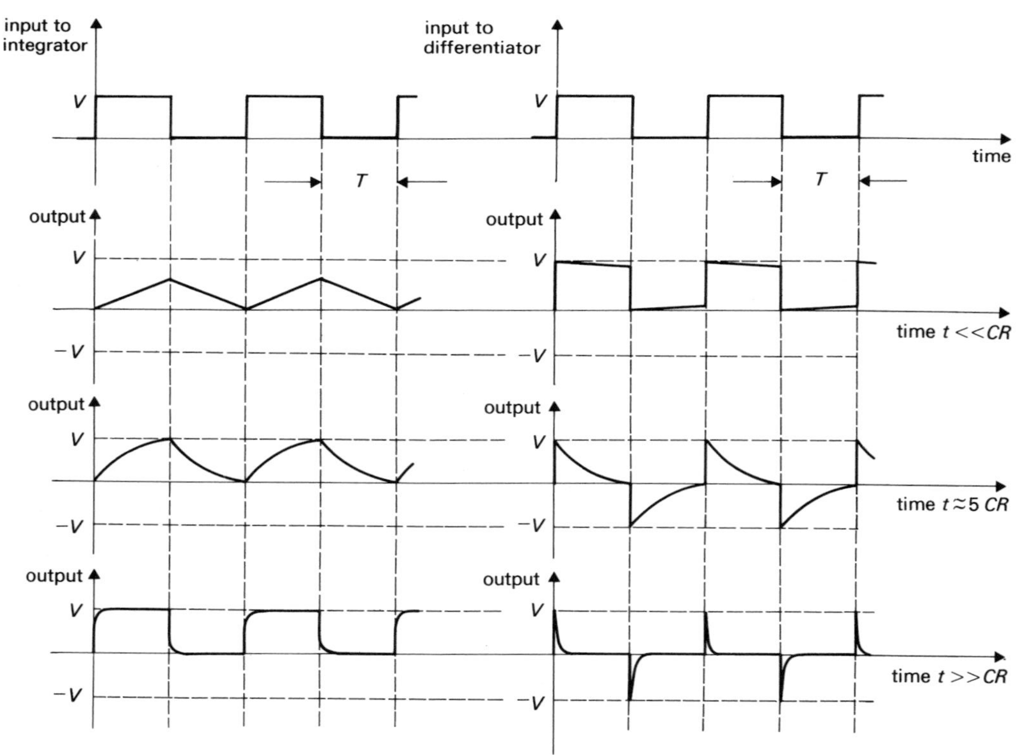

Figure 105 Solution to Self-assessment question 7

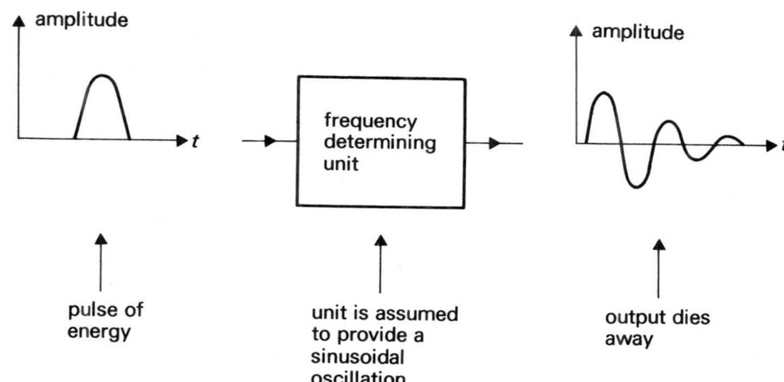

Figure 107 Pulse of energy applied to frequency determining unit

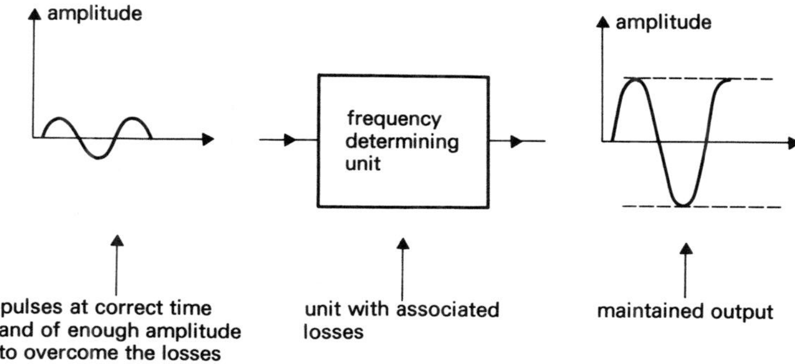

Figure 108 Maintained oscillatory unit

Identification of oscillators

Switching

The energy loss in the frequency determining unit is replaced from a d.c. source where an *electronic switch* ensures that the energy is applied at the correct time in the oscillatory cycle. It normally consists of two interdependent circuits such that the output of each circuit controls the input of the other. This type is known as a *relaxation oscillator*.

Feedback

The output from the frequency determining unit is fed back to its own input in such a sense that the feedback signal aids the change of signal at the input. The energy loss is supplied by an amplifier, and in this case no input signal is required as the frequency determining unit provides its own signal via the feedback network. This type is known as a *feedback oscillator.*

Negative resistance

The oscillations which normally die away in a non-maintained circuit due to resistance could continue indefinitely if the resistance is eliminated. The loss replacement section can be regarded as negative resistance; when added to the resistance of the frequency determining unit it just cancels it out, thus providing the conditions for maintained oscillation. This type is known as a *negative resistance oscillator.*

Applications of oscillators

Relaxation oscillator

These are based around the monostable, bistable and astable devices. The use of 'mono' and 'bi' describes the number of available stable states in which the circuit stays until an external trigger pulse is applied. Thus the monostable can be in one stable state only, and the bistable can be in either of two stable states only. The astable circuit has no stable states and switches continuously between states.

Feedback oscillator

These are normally arranged to provide a sinewave output. They are used in transmitters to provide the carrier frequency for the modulator, and in receivers to provide the carrier frequency for the demodulator. They are also used in test instruments where the generation of sinewaves is required.

Negative resistance oscillator

These are also used where sinewave outputs are required. A typical example is the use of a crystal oscillator and a tunnel diode to counteract the energy loss within the crystal. Further details of this type of oscillator are investigated later in this topic area.

A range of oscillator uses is shown in Table 9. It must be emphasized that the table is by no means exhaustive, but gives an indication only of the range of uses that the oscillator has in electronics.

Types of feedback

In the topic area Feedback, two simple types of feedback (i.e. positive and negative feedback) were identified. The effects of negative feedback were closely investigated, but other than defining positive

application		waveform	use
radio transmitters		sinusoidal	generation and control of r.f. signal at high accuracy
radio receivers		sinusoidal	production of r.f. signal to heterodyne with incoming signal to produce the i.f.
signal generators		sinusoidal square	production of accurately known test signals
television receivers oscilloscopes		sawtooth	production of CRT scanning waveforms
computing logic digital	monostable	single pulse	generation and shaping of pulse to standard form or for delay circuits
	bistable	either of two pulses	two state device for logic applications i.e. registers, memories, etc.
	astable	continuous pulses	pulse train generation, source for wave shaping, tone generation etc.
radar transmitters		staccato pulses	detection
radar receivers		staccato pulses	detection

Table 9 Simple outline of a few uses of oscillators

feedback, its effects on circuits were not considered. When an amplifier is used to provide feedback that increases the system gain by aiding the input signal to the amplifier (positive feedback), either of the two methods shown in Figure 109 may be used.

(1) If a non-inverting amplifier (or two inverting amplifiers connected in cascade) is used and the output fed back to the input, the feedback is positive. This is illustrated in Figure 109(*a*).

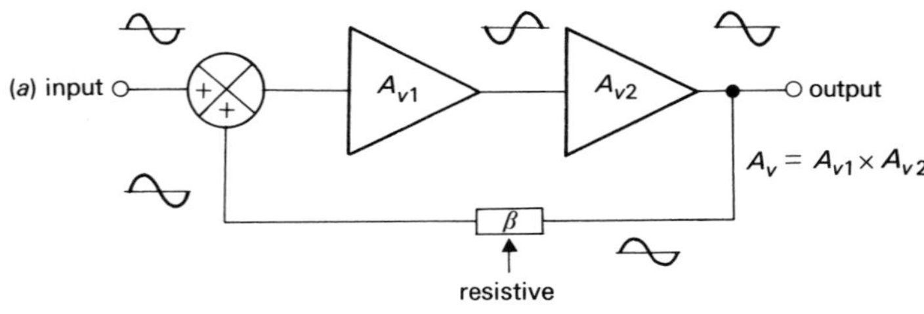

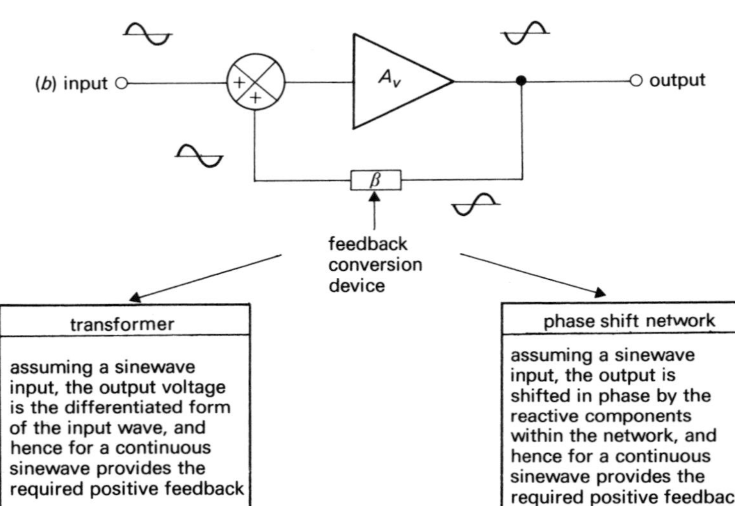

Figure 109 Amplifiers and feedback

(2) If an inverting amplifier is used, the feedback coupling system is made to change the output waveform so that it aids the input signal. This ensures positive feedback. It can be done by using either a transformer or a phase shift network, as shown in Figure 109(*b*).

Whichever of these systems is used, each has an associated inductance and capacitance. The effect of inductance and capacitance can be investigated by considering the general feedback equation.

$$G_v = \frac{A_v}{1 - A_v\beta} \qquad (1$$

Case a	for a non-inverting amplifier	A_v is positive
	resistive feedback network	β is positive

Substituting in equation 1 gives

$$G_v = +\frac{A_v}{1 - A_v\beta}$$

Case b using	for an inverting amplifier	A_v is negative
either	a phase shifting network (180°)	β is negative
or	a transformer to provide the correct polarity of feedback	β is negative

Substituting in equation 1 gives

$$G_v = -\frac{A_v}{1-(A_v)(-\beta)} = -\frac{A_v}{1-A_v\beta}$$

Hence, for these cases only

$$G_v = \pm\frac{A_v}{1-A_v\beta}$$

The plus or minus sign indicates if the amplifier is inverting or non-inverting

Consider for these cases the open loop gain $A_v\beta$. If the feedback is connected so that:

$A_v\beta < 1$ (i) the gain of the system increases.

$A_v\beta = 1$ (ii) the system oscillates with constant amplitude at the output providing oscillations are started by some external factor, e.g. noise.

$A_v\beta > 1$ (iii) the system oscillates spontaneously and the amplitude of oscillations increases until the amplifier limits such that $A_v\beta = 1$.

β	A_v	$A_v\beta$	G_v	v_{in} (volts)
$\frac{1}{50}$	5	$\frac{1}{10}$	5·56	0·179
$\frac{1}{50}$	10	$\frac{1}{5}$	12·5	0·08
$\frac{1}{50}$	20	$\frac{2}{5}$	33·3	0·03
$\frac{1}{50}$	30	$\frac{3}{5}$	75·0	0·013
$\frac{1}{50}$	40	$\frac{4}{5}$	200	0·005
$\frac{1}{50}$	50	1·0	∞	zero

Table 10 Calculations to show effect of frequency change

v_{in} is the input voltage required to produce an output voltage of 1 V for an oscillator containing a non-inverting type amplifier.

To see the implication of this more clearly, consider the calculations contained in Table 10, which shows the input voltage required to produce an output voltage of 1 V for a non-inverting amplifier type oscillator. At low frequencies the system is not oscillating, and at the lowest frequency A_v is measured as 5. The mid-band gain A_v is 100, and the feedback fraction β is $\frac{1}{50}$ and is provided by high stability

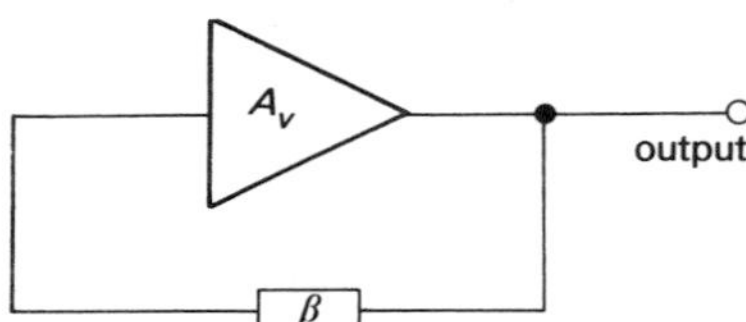

Figure 110 Oscillator system with no input

resistors. The frequency of the input signal is increases such that th gain A_v begins to increase. The values of A_v are shown as measured G_v is found from

$$G_v = +\frac{A_v}{1 - A_v\beta}$$

and $$v_{in} = \frac{v_{out}}{G_v}$$

From the table it can be seen that

(i) For $A_v = 50$ the gain is infinite

(ii) The input voltage to produce an output of 1 V is zero volts. Thus, no input is required for an oscillator system for values of A > 50. This is shown in the system diagram of Figure 110.

For any feedback system, the general feedback equation is

$$G_v = \frac{A_v}{1 - A_v\beta}$$

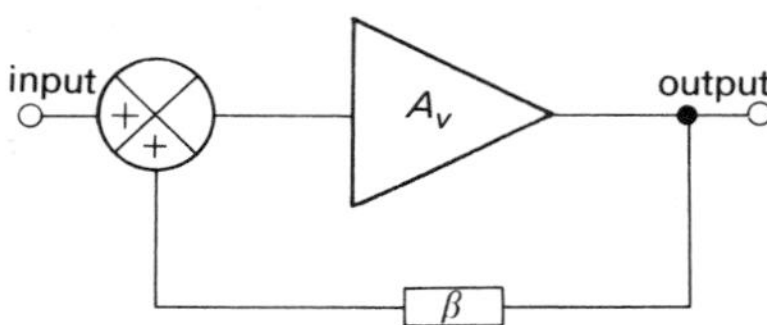

Figure 111 Amplifier with feedback

For the amplifier shown in Figure 111, unless values of A_v and β ar known both in magnitude and phase, the type of feedback applied cannot be stipulated.

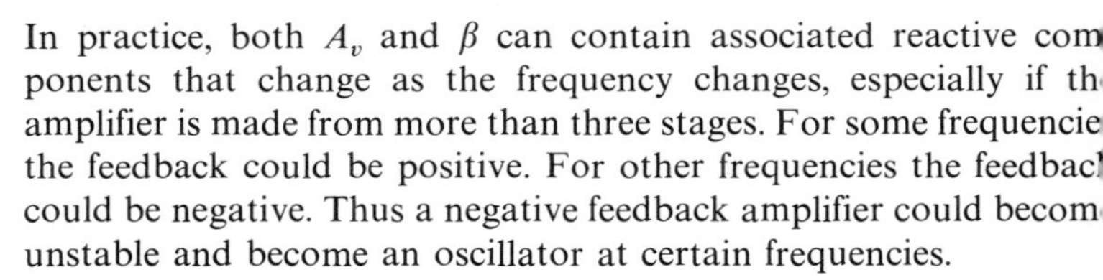

In practice, both A_v and β can contain associated reactive com ponents that change as the frequency changes, especially if th amplifier is made from more than three stages. For some frequencie the feedback could be positive. For other frequencies the feedbac could be negative. Thus a negative feedback amplifier could becom unstable and become an oscillator at certain frequencies.

N.B. For feedback cases other than those quoted much mor sophisticated design techniques are used to investigate the stability o the system. These techniques are beyond the levels set by th Electronics 3 TEC objectives.

If the associated reactances of the circuits shown in Figure 109 ar pre-determined (and not left to chance circuit reactances), th frequency of the output sinewave can be more carefully controlled Thus to be of practical use a sinewave oscillator requires a frequenc determining network; in general the two types of circuits used ar shown in Figure 112.

The *LC* oscillator can have the coupling system and the frequenc determining unit interchanged. Thus for a feedback oscillator t produce maintained oscillations

(i) the signal fed back should be of such a phase (related to the inpu signal) that it aids the input signal: positive feedback

(ii) the aiding signal fed back should have enough magnitude to ensur that maintained oscillations take place.

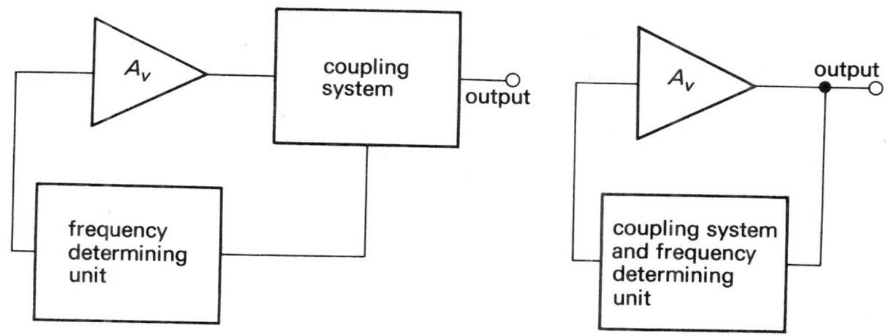

Figure 112 Types of systems for sinusoidal feedback oscillators

The first condition implies that the output signal from the loss replacement unit must be corrected in phase such that it aids the input to the frequency determining circuit.

The second condition implies that when an amplifier is used, the gain of the amplifier multiplied by the combined attenuation of the frequency determining circuit and the coupling system, must be greater than unity. Another way of saying this is that the open loop gain is greater than unity, or $A_v\beta > 1$.

Tuned LC oscillator

It has previously been explained in Electronics 2 that the main requirements of a tuned *LC* circuit for use as a frequency determining unit are high selectivity and low loss. To achieve this the resistance of the coil is made low compared with the reactance of the coil at the oscillatory frequency. Another way of saying this is that the coil of the tuned *LC* circuit must have a high *Q* factor. This is a requirement of tuned circuits at radio frequencies. However it becomes difficult to construct a physically small tuned circuit of high *Q* factor at audio frequencies because of the component values required. At these low frequencies a.f. feedback oscillators of the *LC* type can produce a distorted output due to poor selectivity. If used at a.f., the purest sinewave in fact is obtained with 'loose' coupling, and to increase output amplitude by 'tightening' the coupling causes distortion to occur.

In fact pure a.f. waveforms are generally obtained using *RC* networks either by a ladder type network where the feedback is progressively adjusted to match the input waveform as shown in Figure 113, or by using a Wien circuit. (This circuit is discussed later in this section.)

In general for frequencies above 1 MHz, tuned *LC* circuits are used as the frequency determining network. For frequencies below this, *RC*

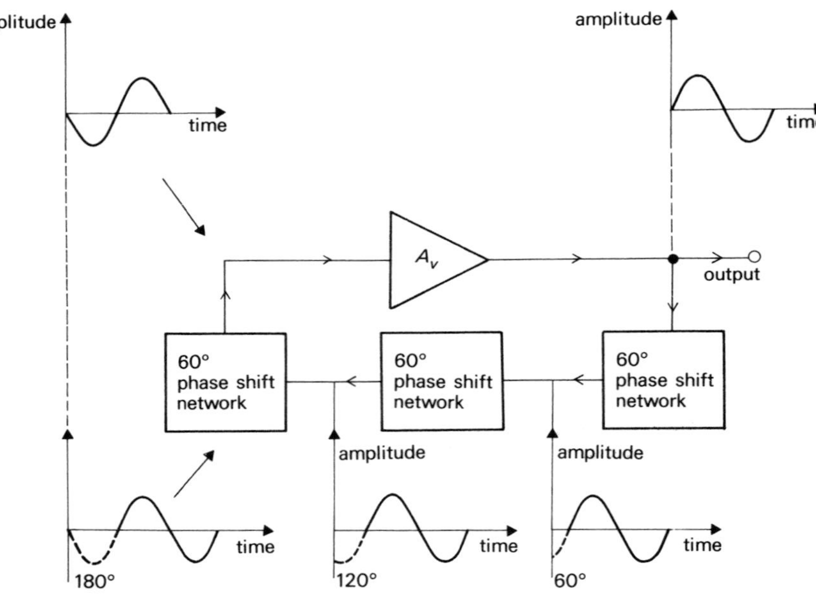

Figure 113 *R C* feedback oscillator using ladder network

networks are used and are the basic oscillator form for most laboratory signal generators (in particular the Wien circuit).

The explanation of the operation of the *LC* oscillator was covered in detail in Electronics 2 when discussing the tuned collector oscillator, thermionic triode oscillator, and methods of applying bias. However, the factors which affect oscillator amplitude stabilization for *LC* oscillators were not discussed. The method adopted depends on the ease of design, the influence of component tolerances, the dependence on the valve or transistor parameters and the method of bias.

Methods of bias

Class A: This method of bias gives the purest sinewave. The d.c. biasing is set to put the quiescent point at the most linear part of the transfer characteristic. Feedback must be sufficient to cause oscillation to start from an infinitesimally small initiating signal such as noise. As the signal increases, the operating point is driven into the nonlinear region; the parameters of the amplifying device change, reducing the gain and halting the increase in amplitude. In general the loop gain is made greater than unity and a special circuit used to limit the amplitude, e.g. temperature controlled negative feedback using a thermistor device.

Class B and class C: These methods are designed to produce excessive feedback so that the amplitude builds up quickly. The nonlinearity in the output causes the quiescent point to move until the circuit parameters are just correct to maintain oscillation. This corresponds to the automatic biasing methods described in Electronics 2. Note also that these circuits are more efficient than the class A type; the purity of the output is maintained by the high selectivity (or high Q factor) of the tuned circuit which removes the distortion.

RC oscillators

There are two main types of RC oscillators that are used in practice. They are called

(*a*) ladder network feedback
(*b*) Wien network feedback.

Ladder network feedback

For the ladder network system shown in Figure 113, if one period of the continuous sinewave is considered at the input of the amplifier, it is inverted at the output. The first phase shift network then moves this inverted waveform through 60°, the second network through another 60° and the third through another 60°. Thus the total phase shift at the output of the ladder network is 180° compared to the output signal of the amplifier.

If the waveform is now considered to be a continuous sinewave, the phase shifting network causes the continuous feedback waveform to aid the input signal. Positive feedback is continuous, as shown in Figure 114.

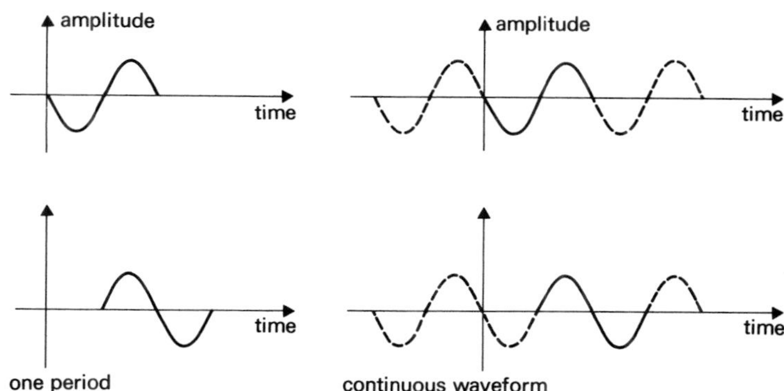

Figure 114 Effect of continuous waveform

Consider the ladder network shown in Figure 115(*a*). It is called a voltage transfer ladder network. For a single *RC* network, the voltage across the capacitor lags the applied voltage by an angle between 0° and 90° (For $R=0$ the angle is 90°; for $C=0$ the angle is 0°).

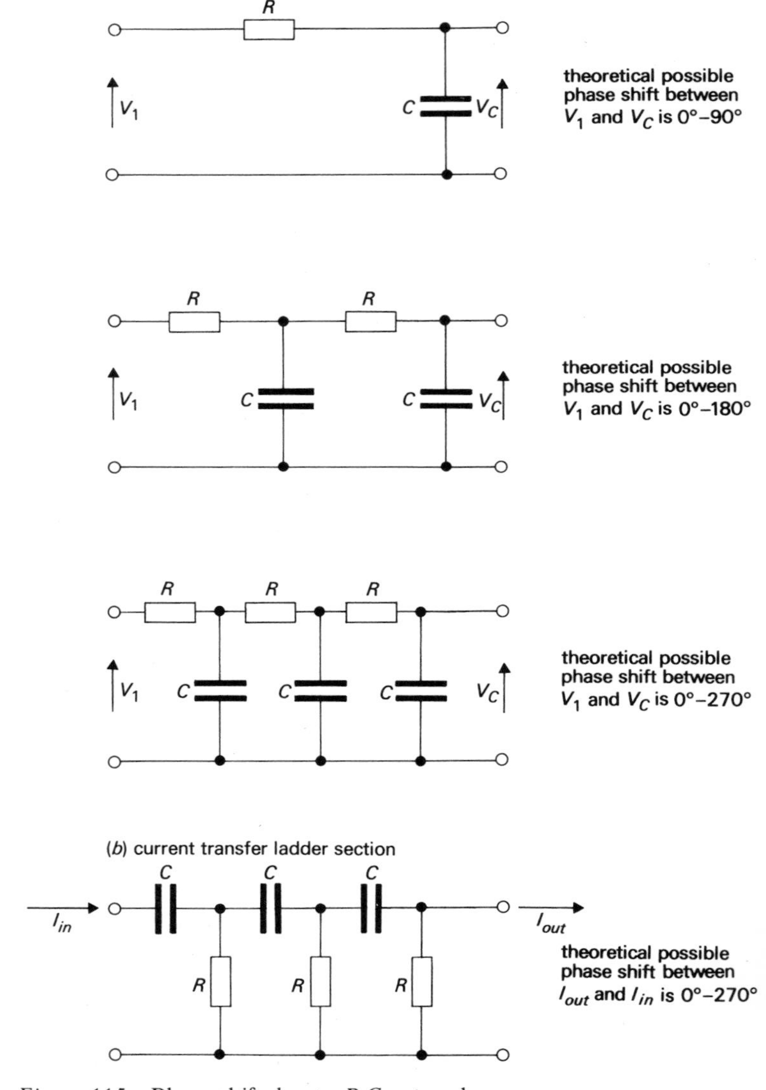

Figure 115 Phase shift due to *R C* network

In practice, an *RC* network always has associated with it some resistance and capacitance. The theoretical values of $R=0$ or $C=0$ are not practicable. Thus for the two networks shown in Figure 115(*a*) a phase shift of 180° is not practically obtainable. For the three networks, a phase shift of 180° is attainable in practice. Another type of ladder can be used; it is shown in Figure 115(*b*). This is known as a current transfer ladder network.

For the voltage transfer ladder, the voltage across the capacitor lags the applied voltage. Thus when the amplifier device has a high input impedance and does not load the network (e.g. a valve or FET device), this is the feedback network used.

For the current transfer ladder, the output current leads the input current. Thus when the amplifier device has a low input impedance (and would load the voltage transfer ladder, as in the case of a transistor) this is the feedback network used.

It can be shown for both these networks that at a frequency given by

$$f=\frac{1}{2\pi(\sqrt{6})RC} \tag{2}$$

the attenuation of the networks is 1/29, and the phase shift at this frequency is 180°.

For oscillation to occur $A_v\beta=1$, and as the magnitude of the feedback fraction is 1/29, the gain of the amplifier must be greater than 29. When the network is used with the amplifier to calculate the frequency of oscillation, the loading effect of the amplifier on the network must be included. In practice, the actual oscillatory frequency is slightly higher than that shown by equation 2.

A typical circuit diagram for an *RC* oscillator using a current transfer ladder feedback and a bipolar transistor is shown in Figure 116.

The transistor is biased for class A operation by the potential divider network R_1 and R_2. The output from the collector is fed to the current transfer ladder network and then to the base of the transistor. To ensure that an adequate current gain is provided for oscillations to occur, the transistor should have an $h_{fe}>60$. In practice the value chosen for R is a compromise and should be such that $h_{ie}>R>h_{oe}$.

Once oscillations have started, the amplitude must be controlled. In the circuit shown, R_E and C_E function in the normal way as previously described. If R_E is made variable and C_E is connected as shown in Figure 117, the effect of introducing a small unbypassed resistive section reduces the base current, and allows control of the output voltage.

Alternatively an emitter follower stage can be inserted between the oscillator and the load, which with all its advantages provided by

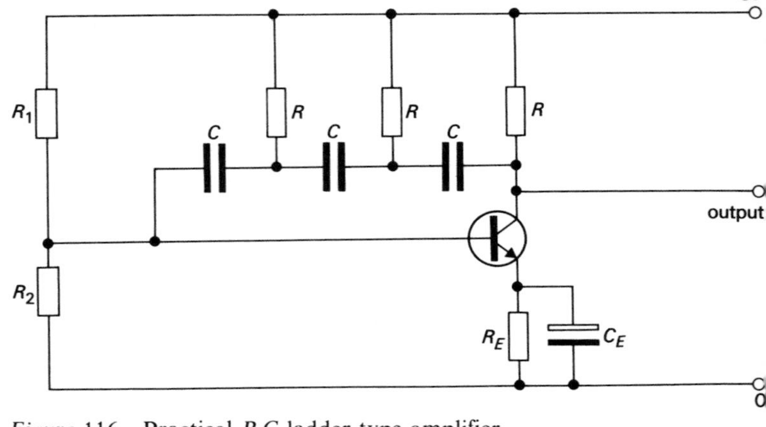

Figure 116 Practical *R C* ladder type amplifier

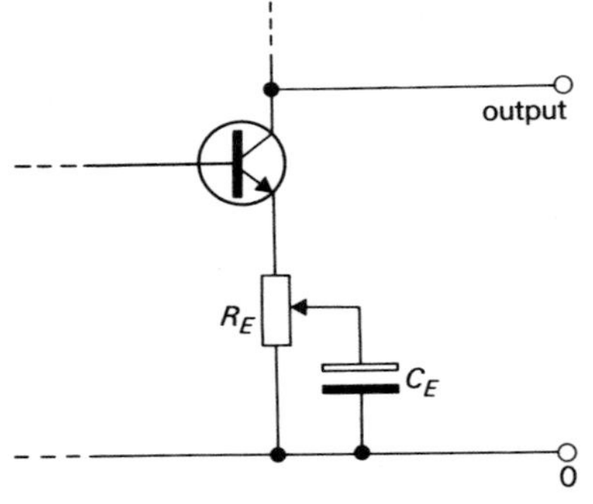

Figure 117 Device to control amplitude of output

large negative feedback, stabilizes the output voltage. These types of oscillator are normally used to provide a fixed frequency output due to the mechanical complexities of ganging the components.

Wien network feedback

A Wien network feedback system is shown in Figure 118. The input signal to the first amplifier is inverted at the output; the output of the first amplifier is inverted by the second amplifier to produce a re-inverted signal. This is fed to the feedback network which, in order to provide the required positive feedback at the input, must introduce no phase shift at all.

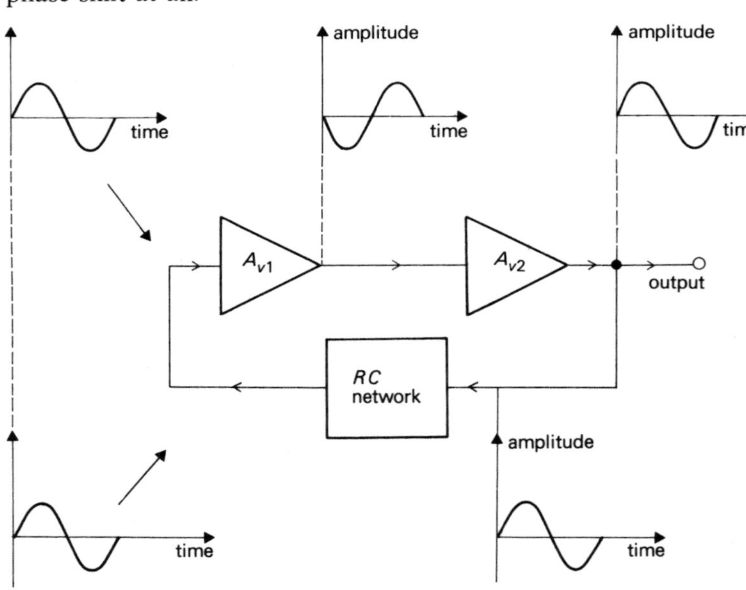

Figure 118 *R C* feedback oscillator using Wien network

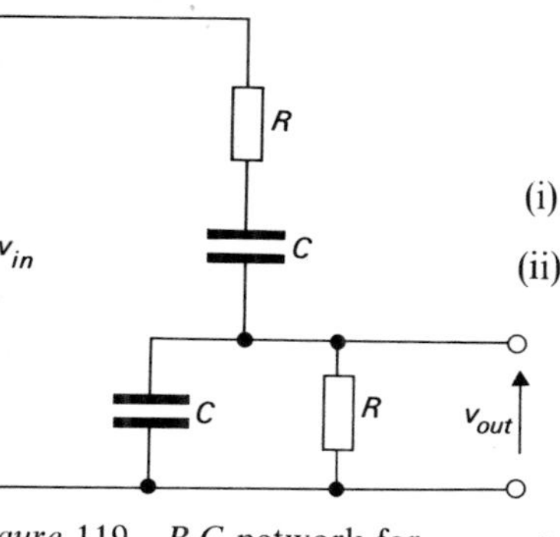

gure 119 *RC* network for
e Wien circuit

For the phase shift network shown in Figure 119, it can be shown that to achieve the necessary positive feedback for oscillation when v_{in} is in phase with v_{out}, the following conditions are required:

(i) $v_{out} = \frac{1}{3} v_{in}$

(ii) frequency of oscillation is $f_r = \dfrac{1}{2\pi CR}$

The network can be used with a non-inverting amplifier (or two amplifiers connected in cascade) to provide the required conditions for oscillation, as shown in Figure 120. The conditions for the *RC* network are satisfied when:

(i) the voltage gain of the amplifier is at least three
(ii) the amplifier is non-inverting
(iii) the input resistance of the amplifier is high compared to *R* in order that the amplifier does not load the *RC* network significantly and alter the required conditions
(iv) the output resistance of the amplifier is low so that the effect of external loading is minimized
(v) there is some method of stabilizing the oscillations.

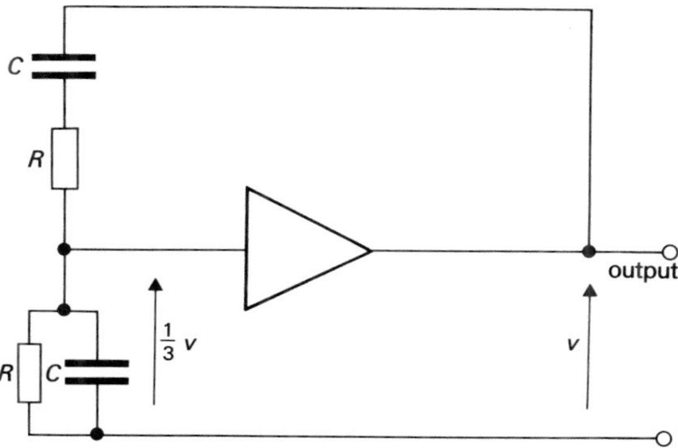

Figure 120 Use of network with non-inverting amplifier

Consider the circuit shown in Figure 121. A two stage amplifier is used so that the total amplification produces the required non-inversion.

The first stage is an FET stage with a high input resistance, where R_1 is the drain load and R_2 is the source resistance, which is not decoupled. The output is coupled via C_2 to the common emitter stage; R_5 is the collector load and R_6 the emitter resistance which is not decoupled. R_2 and R_6 are not decoupled (bypassed) because, for this application, a high value of gain is not required.

The output from the second stage is connected across the Wien network, and the mid-point of the network is connected to the input of the first stage. If the overall gain of the two stages is greater than 3, the circuit oscillates. The amplitude of the oscillations is stabilized by

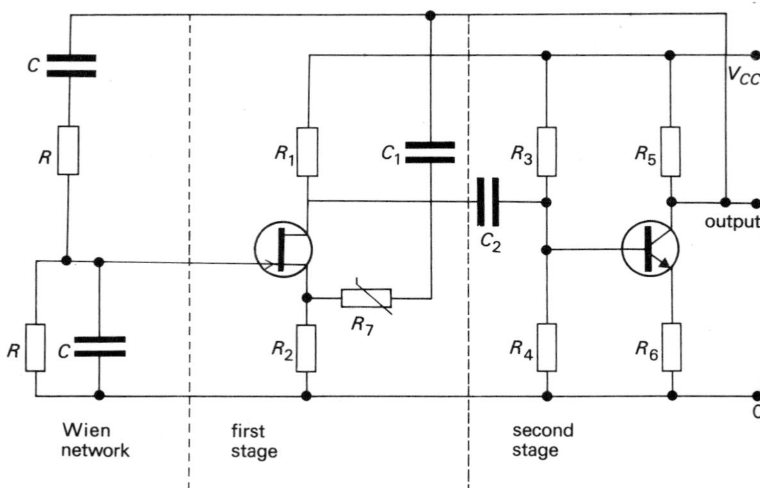

Figure 121 Practical circuit of a Wien oscillator

thermistor R_7 which provides negative feedback through C_1. When the circuit is switched on, the thermistor has a high value and little feedback is applied; thus the amplifier has high enough gain for oscillations to begin. As these oscillations increase, more power is dissipated in R_7 and its resistance decreases. When R_7 decreases such that the overall gain is 3, the amplitude of the oscillations remains constant. If the gain falls for any reason, the thermistor value increases, allowing the gain to increase and stabilize once more to an overall value of 3.

It should be noted that the output has a very pure sinusoidal waveform, and because of the large amount of negative feedback which can be applied to bring the overall gain of the two stages to 3, a high degree of frequency stability is obtained. For a variable frequency output, the two capacitors can be mounted on one spindle or the resistors can be ganged together. However the frequency range must then be limited (since R must be kept much less than the amplifier input resistance).

Stability considerations of oscillator

The general representation of an oscillator is illustrated in diagrammatic form in Figure 122. It can be seen that the frequency of the oscillator may vary due to a number of external factors.

Effect of temperature variation

Values of R, L and C vary with temperature, the most temperature

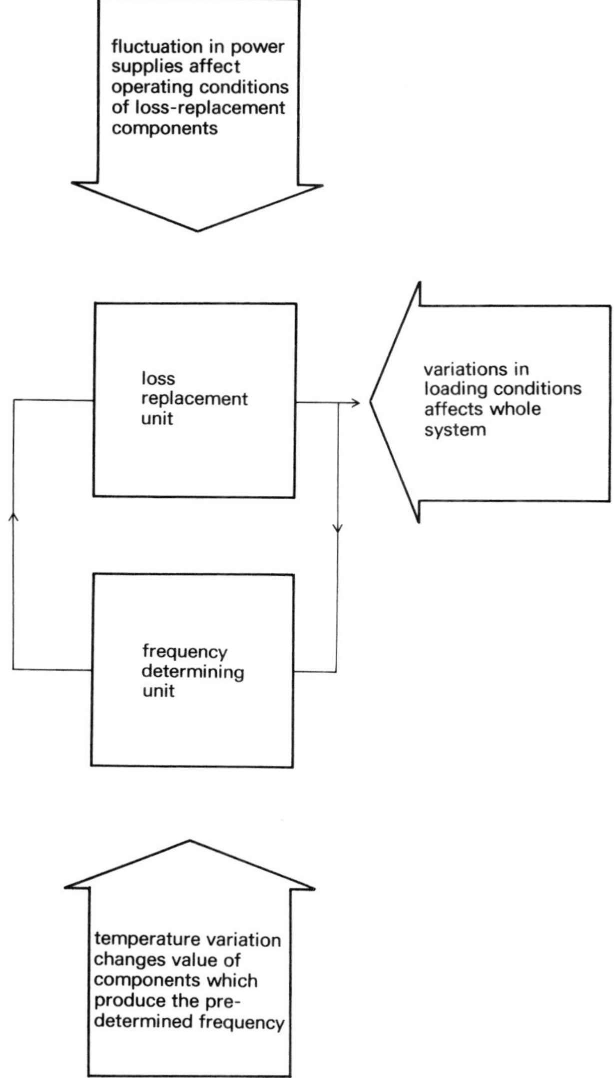

Figure 122 External factors affecting frequency

sensitive of which is the capacitance. The capacitive effect is reduced by using:

(i) a compensating capacitor (shunting the main tuning capacitor) whose mechanical design provides temperature compensation
(ii) capacitors with low temperature coefficients, or a combination of capacitors with positive and negative coefficients
(iii) a constant temperature enclosure
(iv) a stabilizing element that is made temperature sensitive in such a manner that ambient temperature variations alter the d.c. conditions.

Thus the amplifier device parameters alter to offset the circuit parameter variation.

Effect of voltage variation

RC oscillators are reasonably independent of supply voltages, since the frequency depends only on the values of components in the circuit.

LC oscillators however are affected by the parameters of the amplifying device, which in turn depend on the supply voltages. This effect can be reduced by:

(i) using stabilized supplies

(ii) using a coil with a high *Q* factor for the tuned circuit, as this reduces the effect of the device parameters on the tuned circuit

(iii) keeping the inductance of the coupling coil as small as possible yet still maintaining oscillations. This has the advantage of improving the waveform purity for class A operation.

Effect of load variations

In general, the loading of the oscillator shunts the frequency determining unit by an impedance which can affect the frequency. The effect can be reduced by two methods:

(i) *LC* oscillators are coupled magnetically by a small coil to the load. Weak coupling ensures that the reflected shunt impedance across the tuned load is small and hence its effect is small. Variations in load impedance have little effect on the oscillatory frequency.

(ii) A buffer amplifier, which is usually a tuned amplifier, is interposed between the oscillator and the load. The oscillator tuned circuit is coupled to the high input impedance of the amplifier and the load is coupled to its output. The effect is to reduce the interaction between the load and oscillator.

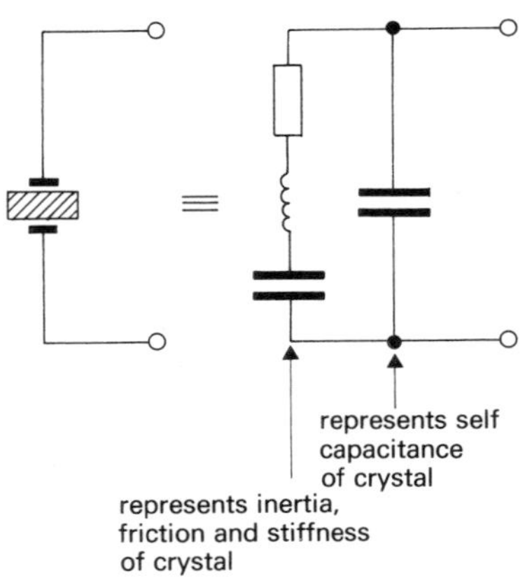

Figure 123 Equivalence of a crystal to a tuned circuit

There is a limit to the stability that can be obtained using normal tuned circuits. For higher stability a crystal oscillator is used. The principle is to use the crystal to resonate mechanically. It replaces the *LC* tuned circuit as shown in Figure 123. The crystal has a resonant frequency similar to that of an electrically tuned circuit, but has a much higher *Q* value with all the advantages mentioned previously. To convert this mechanical vibration to electrical energy, the crystal exhibits a piezoelectric effect, i.e. the mechanical vibration sets up an electrical force across the crystal faces or vice versa. Each crystal is cut so that it has a characteristic frequency pre-determined by its physical characteristics. It cannot be used at any other frequency. Typical frequencies range from approximately 4 kHz to 10 MHz. The stability of the crystal is of a high order, and a frequency accuracy of 1 part in 10^6 can be maintained for long periods. For increased accuracy the crystal is maintained in a temperature-controlled oven.

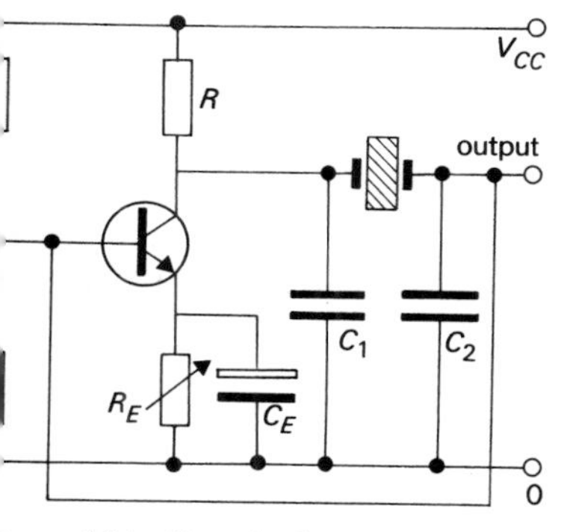

gure 124 Practical crystal cillator circuit

As the equivalent circuit has three reactive components, it has two resonant frequencies. The lowest is a series type resonant frequency, while the highest is a parallel type resonant frequency.

Consider the circuit shown in Figure 124 which is designed around the common emitter stage. This stage causes the input signal to the base of the transistor to be inverted. The output signal at the collector is then taken via a 180° phase shifting network, which includes the crystal operating in the series resonant mode, and fed back to the input. The signal thus aids the input and provides the required positive feedback. R_1 and R_2 bias the transistor for class A operation; R_E is adjusted so that the loop gain is slightly greater than unity, and oscillations build up until the effective gain has stabilized to unity. C_1 and C_2 are made as large as possible so that the frequency of oscillation approximates to the series resonant mode, and is not dependent on C_1 and C_2. However, C_1 and C_2 shunt the output of the transistor and reduce the feedback signal. Thus the gain of the transistor limits the maximum values of C_1 and C_2. Also, the output amplitude should be kept low to avoid excessive power dissipation in the crystal. This avoids the 'ageing' that the crystal undergoes.

Self-assessment questions

Complete the following sentences related to oscillators either by writing in the correct word or deleting the incorrect word where applicable.

1 The purpose of an oscillator is to produce an output signal that:
(*a*) changes magnitude/frequency between stated levels
(*b*) produces a random/recurring waveshape at the required frequency.

2 The type of oscillator that applies feedback from the output of an amplifier to aid the amplifier input signal via a frequency determining unit is called a ____________ oscillator.

3 The type of oscillator that consists of two interdependent circuits such that the output of each circuit controls the input of the other is called a ____________ oscillator.

4 The type of oscillator that has a loss replacement unit which has a negative resistance is known as a ____________ ____________ oscillator.

5 State two common uses of the
(*a*) Feedback oscillator
(*b*) Relaxation oscillator.

6 State the two parts that an oscillator must have to function properly

Complete Questions 7–22 related to oscillators either by writing in the correct word(s) or deleting the incorrect word where applicable

7 When a small proportion of the output signal of an amplifier is coupled back to the input signal such that it aids the input signal negative/positive feedback is applied.

8 When a small proportion of the output signal of an amplifier is coupled back to the input signal such that it opposes the input signal negative/positive feedback is applied.

9 A sinewave oscillator is an amplifier with positive feedback sufficient to ____________ its own output.

10 The two basic requirements of a sinewave oscillator to produce maintained oscillations are

(i) ____________

(ii) ____________

11 For a feedback oscillator $G_v = \pm \frac{A_v}{1 - A_v\beta}$

(*a*) For $A_v\beta < 1$ the gain of the system increases/decreases

(*b*) For $A_v\beta = 1$ the system oscillates with constant ____________ providing oscillations are started by some external ____________

(*c*) For $A_v\beta > 1$ the system oscillates ____________.

12 For a feedback amplifier that is made from a number of circuit stages

(*a*) the feedback is always positive

TRUE/FALSE

(*b*) the feedback is always negative

TRUE/FALSE

(*c*) the feedback can be either positive or negative depending on the frequency of the input signal

TRUE/FALSE

13 At audio/radio frequencies the physical size of the components required make construction difficult for a high *Q* tuned circuit.

14 *RC* networks are generally used to obtain pure r.f./a.f. sinusoidal waveforms.

15 For *LC* tuned circuit oscillators the purest sinewave is obtained when the amplifier is biased under class A/class C operating conditions

16 Class C operating conditions are arranged to produce excessive/minimal feedback at the instant when the feedback oscillator is switched on.

17 Under correct operating conditions the ladder network produces zero/180° phase shift from input to output.

18 Under correct operating conditions the Wien network produces zero/180° phase shift from input to output.

19 The amplifier used in the Wien network feedback oscillator is inverting/non-inverting.

20 The amplifier used in the ladder network feedback oscillator is inverting/non-inverting.

21 The minimum theoretical gain for the amplifier used in the Wien network feedback oscillator to maintain oscillations is ___________.

22 The minimum theoretical gain for the amplifier used in the ladder network feedback oscillator to maintain oscillations is ___________.

23 State the three main factors that affect the frequency stability of oscillators.

24 State a method to improve each of the three factors of Question 23.

25 State the main advantage of the piezo-crystal oscillator over the tuned *LC* circuit.

26 State the reason for the advantage stated for Question 25.

27 Explain the circuit operation of the circuit shown in Figure 124 in terms of the frequency determining unit, the loss replacement section, and positive feedback.

In the following questions tick the correct answer.

28 The purpose of a buffer amplifier connected to the output of an oscillator is to provide
(*a*) The energy to maintain oscillations
(*b*) Frequency stability as the temperature varies
(*c*) Frequency stability as the loading conditions varies
(*d*) Inversion of the input signal and hence positive feedback to the input of the amplifier.

29 The type of oscillator generally used to produce a train of rectangular pulses is called a
(*a*) Feedback oscillator
(*b*) Relaxation oscillator
(*c*) Negative resistance oscillator
(*d*) Sinewave oscillator.

30 Which of the following units are required to build a feedback oscillator that produces a sinewave output signal where frequency stability is not important?
(*a*) Inverting amplifier, tuned circuit, buffer amplifier
(*b*) Inverting amplifier, crystal, buffer amplifier
(*c*) Non-inverting amplifier, tuned circuit
(*d*) Inverting amplifier, tuned circuit.

31 In a phase shift *RC* network transistor oscillator
(*a*) The frequency determining network is transformer coupled
(*b*) Feedback is taken direct from emitter to base
(*c*) The frequency is controlled by varying the inductance of the frequency determining network
(*d*) The required phase shift is produced by the *RC* network.

32 Delete the incorrect words.
For high selectivity in an *LC* tuned circuit the resistance/reactance of the coil should be low compared with its resistance/reactance.

33

Type of amplifier	Feedback phase shift
A Inverting	0°
B Inverting	180°
C Non-inverting	0°
D Non-inverting	180°

Match the types of amplifier with their phase shift labelled A..D to the following types of oscillators labelled (*a*)..(*e*).
(*a*) *RC* ladder network oscillator
(*b*) Wien network oscillator
(*c*) Single stage amplifier and tuned *LC* circuit
(*d*) Two stage amplifier and tuned *LC* circuit
(*e*) Single stage amplifier and crystal tuned oscillator.

34 Underline the correct answer.
(*a*) *RC* oscillators are used mainly at r.f. TRUE/FALSE
(*b*) *LC* oscillators are used mainly at a.f. TRUE/FALSE
(*c*) *RC* oscillators are used where a wide frequency range is required TRUE/FALSE
(*d*) *LC* oscillators are easily constructed for typical a.f. use TRUE/FALSE

After reading the following material, the reader shall:

9 Describe the action of transistor multivibrators.
9.1 State the requirements of a transistor multivibrator.
9.2 Describe the three different types of multivibrator:
(*a*) Astable
(*b*) Monostable
(*c*) Bistable.
9.3 Explain the term pulse duty factor.
9.4 Describe the action of the three different types of multivibrator by deriving waveforms present around the circuits.
9.5 Explain the need for synchronizing and triggering multivibrators.
9.6 State the methods of triggering and synchronizing multivibrators.

The main requirement of a transistor multivibrator is to produce rectangular waveforms that are close to the theoretical rectangular shape with the minimum distortion possible required for the particular desired circuit function. The three types of multivibrator are described as astable, monostable or bistable.

Astable device

As stated previously, the output from a relaxation oscillator is non-sinusoidal. Positive feedback is used but the feedback coupling is very 'tight'. This results in much more abrupt changes in output which cause the amplifiers to operate more like switches. One example of the relaxation oscillator is the multivibrator or astable oscillator. The amplifiers are used as shown in Figure 126 to obtain the correct conditions for positive feedback, the abrupt changes being brought about by the high level of feedback employed. The output is a series of pulses or square waves as shown in Figure 125. The on/off times of the square waves do not need to be equal; switch 1 can be arranged to operate faster than switch 2 or vice-versa.

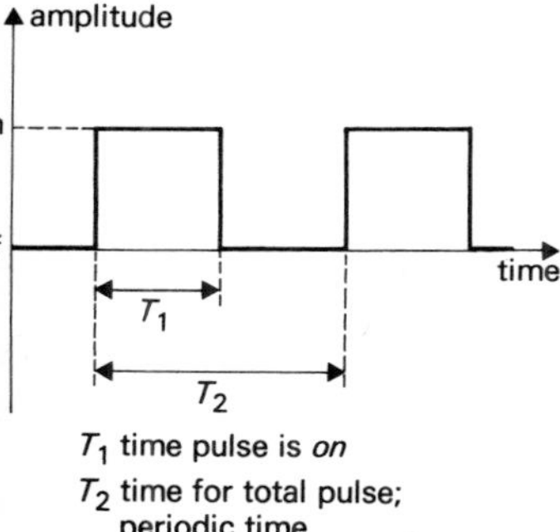

ure 125 The pulse duty factor

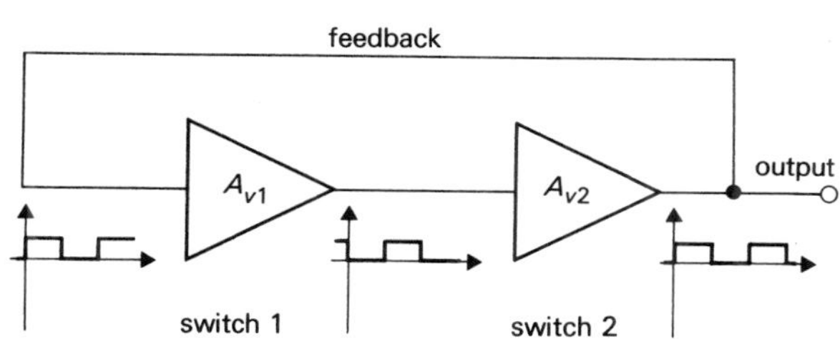

Figure 126 Amplifiers used as switches

Solutions to self-assessment questions (pages 131–134)

1 The purpose of an oscillator is to produce an output signal that
(*a*) Changes magnitude between stated levels
(*b*) Produces a recurring waveshape at the required frequency.

2 The type of oscillator is called a feedback oscillator.

3 The type of oscillator is called a relaxation oscillator.

4 The type of oscillator is called a negative resistance oscillator.

5
(*a*) Modulators, demodulators or test instruments
(*b*) Pulse train generators, time base generators or timing circuits.

6 To function properly an oscillator must have
(*a*) a frequency determining unit
(*b*) a loss replacement unit.

7 Positive feedback is applied.

8 Negative feedback is applied.

9 Maintain.

10 The signal fed back should
(i) aid the input signal
(ii) have enough magnitude to ensure maintained oscillations occur.

11
(*a*) Increases.
(*b*) Amplitude, factor.
(*c*) Spontaneously.

12
(*a*) FALSE.
(*b*) FALSE.
(*c*) TRUE because the type of feedback can vary as the frequency varies.

13 At audio frequencies the physical size of the components required makes construction difficult for a high Q tuned circuit.

14 RC networks are generally used to obtain pure a.f. sinusoidal waveforms.

15 For LC tuned circuit oscillators the purest sinewave is obtained when the amplifier is biased under class A conditions.

16 Class C operating conditions are arranged to produce excessive feedback at the instant when the feedback oscillator is switched on.

17 Under correct operating conditions the ladder network produces 180° phase shift.

18 Under correct operating conditions the Wien network produces zero phase shift from input to output.

19 The amplifier used in the Wien phase shift network is non-inverting.

20 The amplifier used in the ladder network feedback oscillator is inverting.

21 3.

22 29.

23 Temperature, supply voltage and loading variation.

24
(*a*) Stabilizing element (temperature sensitive to ambient temperature change) or constant temperature enclosure
(*b*) Stabilized power supplies or using high Q coils
(*c*) Buffer amplifier connected between oscillator and load.

25 Improved frequency stability.

26 The very high Q factor attainable gives improved selectivity.

27 Frequency determining unit: This is a 180° phase shifting network which includes the crystal. The crystal is operated in the series resonant mode.
Loss replacement section: This is a common emitter amplifier which provides the inversion at the output of an input signal applied to the transistor base.
Positive feedback: The feedback network is adjusted to provide an open loop gain of slightly more than unity. The phase shift of 180° in the feedback network ensure, for a continuous sinewave, that the feedback signal aids the input to provide the required positive feedback.

28 (*c*).

29 (*b*).

30 (*c*) None of the others provide conditions for positive feedback.

31 (*d*).

32 For high selectivity in an LC circuit the resistance of the coil should be low compared with its reactance.

33
(*a*) B.
(*b*) C.
(*c*) B.
(*d*) C.
(*e*) B.

34
(*a*) FALSE.
(*b*) FALSE.
(*c*) TRUE.
(*d*) FALSE.

The switching times were defined in Electronics 2 in terms of the mark to space ratio, which is now called the pulse duty factor (p.d.f.), and is defined as

$$\text{p.d.f.} = \frac{\text{mark}}{\text{mark} + \text{space}} = \frac{T_1}{T_2}$$

This is shown for the waveform in Figure 125. It can be seen from the above formula that the p.d.f. is less than unity, except under d.c. conditions when the p.d.f. equals unity.

The circuit diagram of Figure 127(*a*) contains two transistors, each being biased by the simple arrangement of connecting R_{B1} and R_{B2} to the base of each transistor T1 and T2 respectively. Both transistors are turned 'hard on' as described in topic area Logic elements and circuits, in Electronics 2. The circuit diagram shown in Figure 127(*b*) has been rearranged when compared with Figure 127(*a*) by moving the resistors R_{B1} and R_{B2} to new positions. This now brings the input of T1 closer to the output of T2, and the input of T2 closer to the output of T1.

The circuit diagram shown in Figure 127(*c*) shows how the feedback components C_1 and C_2 are connected from output to input; the circuit is then complete. How will this affect the stable circuit of Figure 127(*a*)? Assuming there is no voltage drop across each transistor in the *on* condition, i.e. V_{CE} is zero, then the circuit is unstable and cannot exist in practice because each transistor base is at zero. Hence the transistors are both *off*, which by a similar reasoning process, is also an impossible condition. What happens when the circuit is switched on?

At the first instant both transistors start to conduct due to the current supplied by R_{B1} and R_{B2}. As no two transistors are perfectly matched, and as a positive going noise pulse could occur on either transistor base, one conducts faster than the other. Assume T1 conducts at the faster rate. This means the T1 collector voltage begins to drop from a high potential to a low potential. This is coupled to the base of T2, and the drop in potential switches T2 to the *off* condition. The collector of T2 is thus positive, reinforcing the switching *on* of T1 via the base of T1. Does the circuit remain in this condition?

The relative potentials are shown in Figure 128, assuming the transistors are perfect switching devices. The *RC* network of R_{B2} connected in series with C_1 is such that C_1 begins to charge up. When this voltage reaches approximately 0·7 V, T2 conducts, to the effect that the T2 collector potential drops to zero. This drop in potential is applied to the base of T1 and turns it *off*; the T2 collector potential is now zero, and thus R_{B2} and C_2 start to charge up until the voltage applied to the base of T1 reaches 0·7 V. The process continues indefinitely until the power supply is switched off. The waveforms at points in the circuit are shown in Figure 129.

The following points should be noted:

(i) It can be seen that at both collectors, the outputs are not perfect pulse waveforms. The rate of rise of the collector voltage is restricted by the

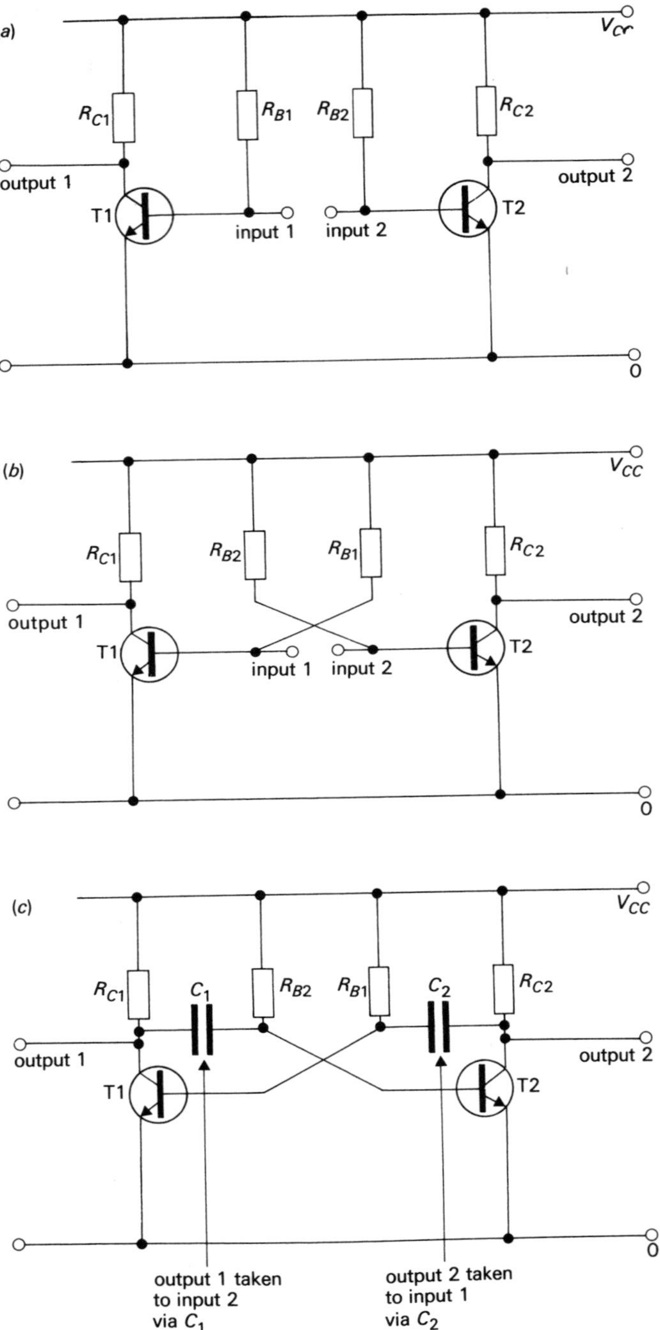

Figure 127 Circuit diagram of the astable oscillator

time constants as indicated on the waveshapes. The waveform can be improved by circuit modification.

(ii) The waveforms shown assume perfect transistor switching characteristics. This is not true in practice; the voltage levels are slightly different from those shown. (For a silicon transistor switching occurs when the base potential rises to about 0·7 V; when saturated $V_{CE} \approx 0{\cdot}2$ V.)

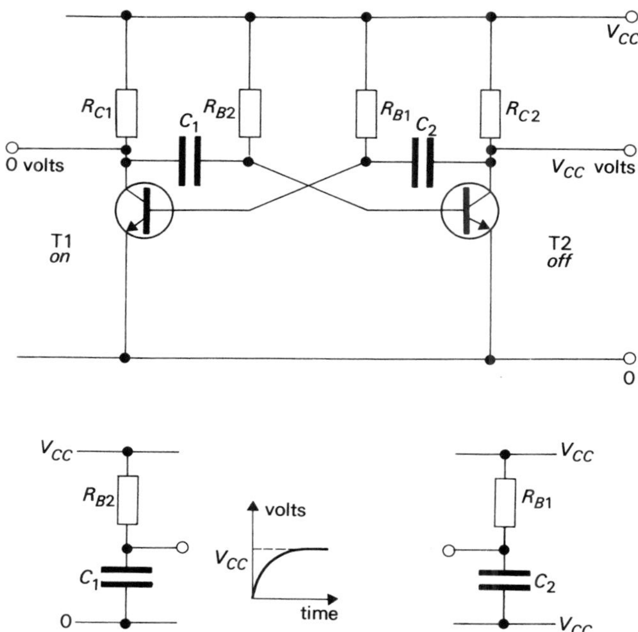

Figure 128 Relative potentials after first instant

(iii) It can be shown that the period for which T1 is cut-off is given by $\tau_1 \approx 0{\cdot}69\ R_{B1}C_2$ and the period for which T2 is cut off is given by $\tau_2 \approx 0{\cdot}69\ R_{B2}C_1$. As $\tau = \tau_1 + \tau_2$ then f can be calculated using the above values. For the particular case when $\tau_1 = \tau_2$ then

$$f = \frac{1}{2 \times 0{\cdot}69 \times CR}$$

where $R = R_{B1} = R_{B2}$
$C = C_1 = C_2$

(iv) Any variation in the external factors changes component values, and thus varies the frequency. If accurate frequency control is required, it is necessary to synchronize the multivibrator output with an accurate frequency source. If synchronizing pulses are applied at the base of one of the transistors as shown in Figure 130, then one of the pulses causes the base voltage to become positive. The transistors are switched at an accurate point defined by the synchronizing pulses, and not the rise time which can vary. Care must be taken with the magnitude and frequency of the synchronizing to ensure that no loss of synchronization occurs.

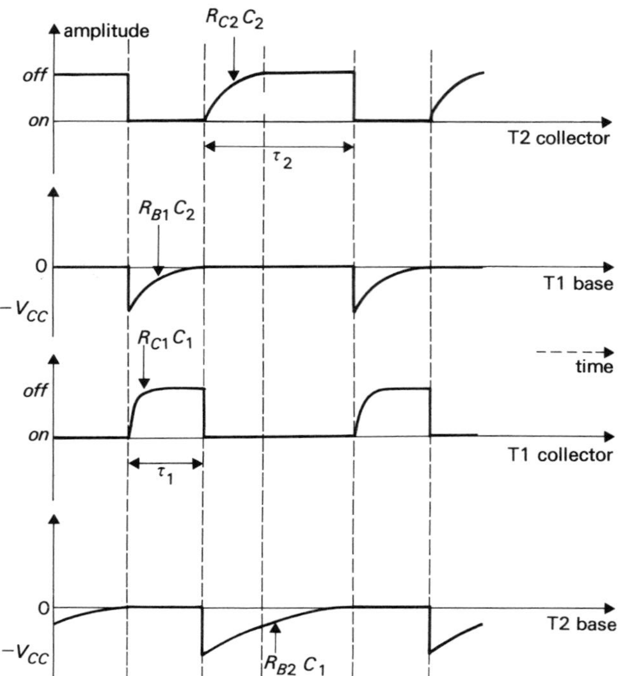

Figure 129 Waveforms at circuit points of the astable circuit assuming steady state conditions

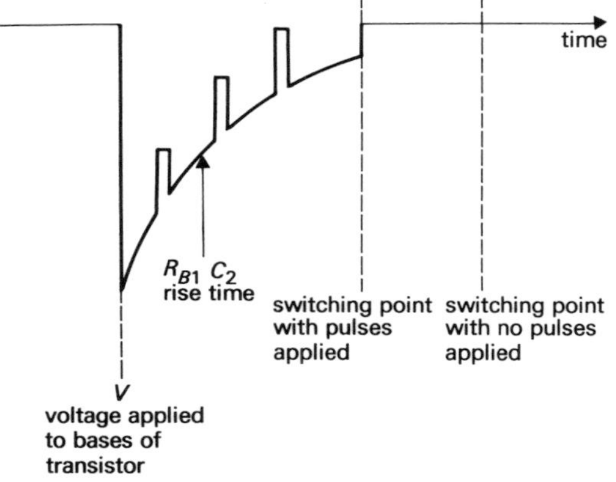

Figure 130 Positive pulses to synchronize the frequency

Monostable device

The circuit of Figure 131 has two modifications when compared with the circuit of Figure 128.

Capacitor C_2 is replaced by a resistor, and R_{B1} is disconnected from the positive supply V_{CC} and connected to a small negative potential $-V_{BB}$.

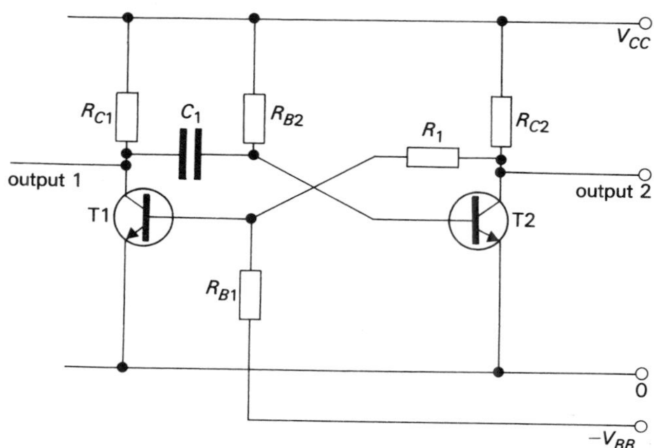

Figure 131 Effect of varying the circuit

When the supply is switched on, T2 is saturated and switched *on* by the base current supplied through R_{B2}. The collector potential of T2 thus falls to almost zero, such that the base of T2 in practice lies somewhere between about 0·2 V and −2 V. Therefore T1 is cut-off, and the potential across the $R_{B2}C_1$ network is zero. The circuit is stable with T1 *off* and T2 *on*. This is the basis of the monostable circuit. What is the effect of applying a trigger input to the base of T1 as shown in Figure 132?

T1 starts to conduct and begins to switch *on*, bringing the collector potential from V_{CC} down towards the zero level. This negative pulse is applied via C_1 to the base of T2 and starts to turn T2 *off*. This brings the collector potential of T2 up towards the V_{CC} level, ensuring that the positive pulse appears at the base of T1 via R_1. The action is regenerative, with the result that T1 is saturated and switched *on* and T2 is switched *off*.

The collector of T1 is now almost at zero potential with the result that the $R_{B2}C_1$ network starts to charge up. When the base of T2 reaches about 0·7 V, T2 starts conducting and the regenerative action switches T2 back *on* and T1 *off*. The time taken for the base of T2 to reach 0·7 V is 0·69 $R_{B2}C_2$. The collector of T1 returns towards V_{CC}

volts with a time constant $R_{C1}C_1$. Thus the time to reach this final value is five time constants. This is the time which must elapse before another pulse can be applied.

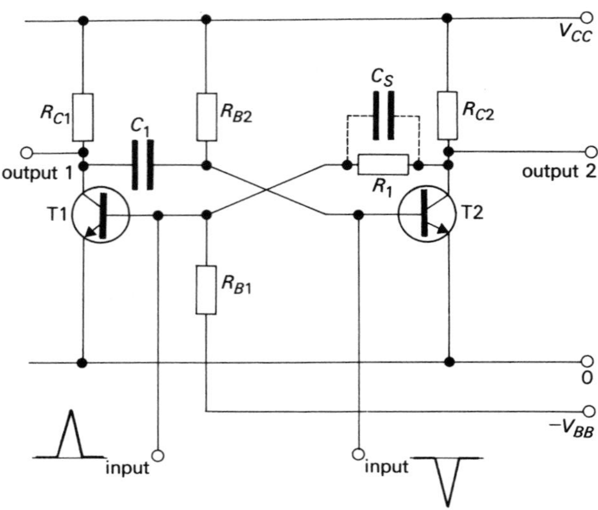

Figure 132 Effect of adding inputs to the circuit

The waveshapes at points in the circuit are shown in Figure 133.

The following points should be noted:

(i) The rate of rise of voltage at output 1 is restricted by the charging time of $R_{C1}C_1$, and the waveform shape is poor. For this reason the output is taken from output 2.

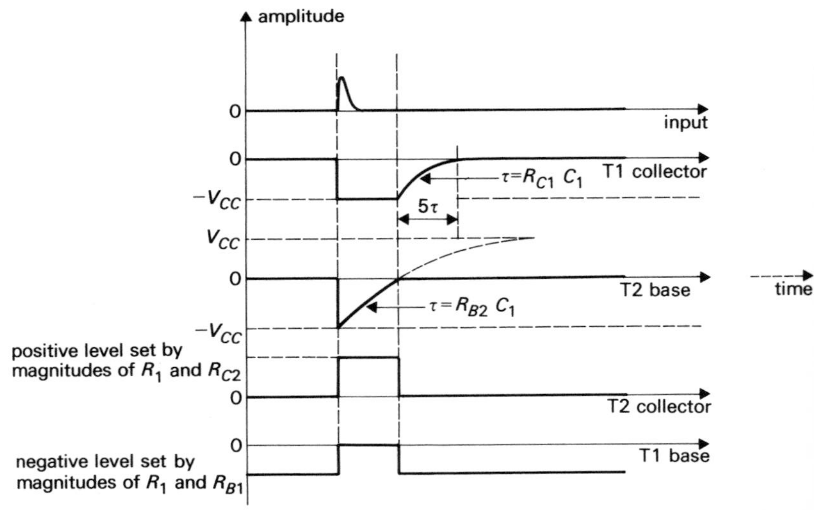

Figure 133 Waveshapes at circuit points of the monostable circuit for a positive input pulse

(ii) The input capacitance of T1 can restrict the rate of rise of the voltage at the base of T1 when T2 turns off suddenly. To compensate for this delay a speed up capacitor C_S is connected across R_1, and normally has a value of a few hundred picofarads.

(iii) The waveforms shown in Figure 133 assume perfect switching characteristics. This is not true in practice, and the voltage levels are slightly different from those shown.

(iv) It can be shown that the period of time the circuit remains in the non-stable state is given by $\tau \approx 0{\cdot}69\ R_{B2}C_1$.

(v) The circuit can be made to function by applying a negative going pulse at the input to the base of T2.

(vi) The circuit converts narrow input pulses to wide output pulses suitable for operating a relay or lamp.

(vii) The circuit converts random shaped input pulses to pulses of standard width as would be required for a rev. counter.

(viii) The circuit can be used to provide a delay if the circuit of Figure 134 is triggered by the negative edge of the output pulse, the length of which can be varied by choice of $R_{B2}C_1$.

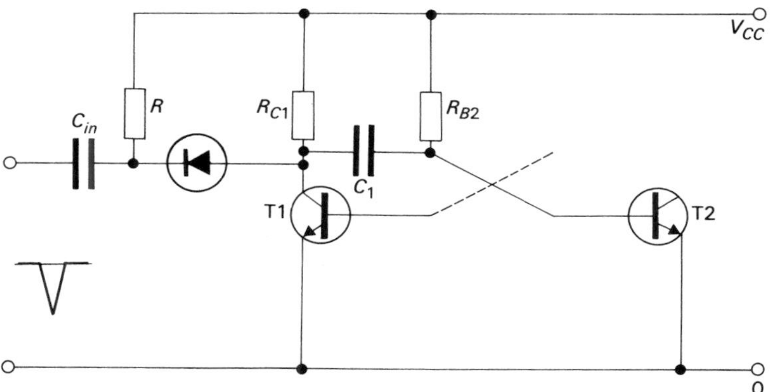

Figure 134 Diode triggering of the monostable circuit

(ix) The circuit is best triggered through a diode as shown in Figure 134. In the stable state T1 is *off* and hence both sides of the diode are at V_{CC}. A negative pulse applied at the input through C_{in} causes the diode to be forward biased. The pulse is fed via C_1 to the base of T2. The use of the diode prevents the source of the triggering voltage upsetting the operation. The diode allows the collector of T1 to drop in potential without feeding back to the pulse source, because the diode is reversed biased and non conducting.

Bistable device

The capacitor C_1 may be replaced by a resistor R, and R_{B1} may be connected to the small negative potential V_{BB}, as shown in Figure 135.

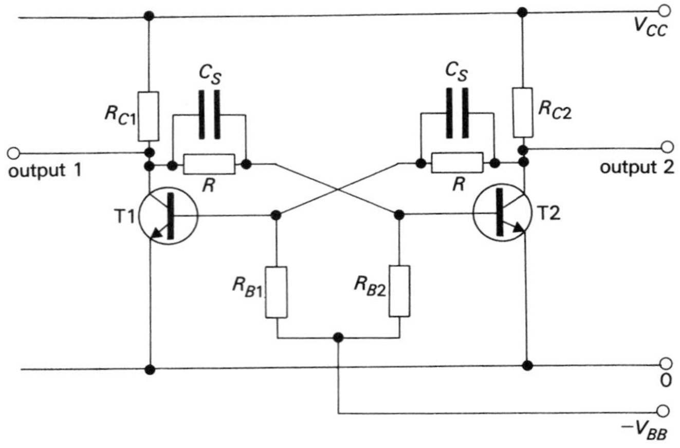

Figure 135 Simple bistable circuit

When the supply is switched on, one transistor conducts before the other, because the two transistors are not identical. This means that if T2 (say) conducts, its collector potential starts to fall to the zero level. This negative change is applied to the base of T1, which means that T2 is *on* and T1 is *off*. In order to accelerate the changeover from one stable state to the other, speed-up capacitors C_S are connected across the resistors R shown in Figure 135. This is the basic circuit of the bistable device.

If the base of T2 is momentarily connected to the zero rail it is cut-off and T1 is switched *on*, even after the connection is removed. In fact this switching process could be carried out by connecting switches from base to emitter of both transistors. It is preferable to switch the circuit by the use of pulses so that the circuit can be used for electronic applications.

It is usual to call the level of voltage a logic condition as described in Electronics 2. Assume positive logic is used, where 0 volts represents logic 0 and V volts represents logic 1. Under these conditions the collector potentials of T1 and T2 can be taken as outputs, which have logic states controlled by input pulses to the device, as shown in the simple circuit of Figure 136.

R	S	$\bar{Q}$	Q
0	0	1	0
0	1	0	1
1	0	0	1
1	1	indeterminate	

Table 11 Truth table for RS bistable

If a positive pulse is applied to the direct set, input T1 is switched *on* and T2 is turned *off*. The bistable is set. Similarly, a positive pulse applied to the direct reset switches T2 *on*, and T1 is turned *off*. The bistable is thus being used as a *one bit memory*. The truth table for this is shown in Table 11.

If pulses are applied to R and S, both at the same time, the output condition is indeterminate. This is because when the pulses are removed, it is not possible to say which transistor stays on while the other one turns off. For this reason it is inadvisable to try to use this

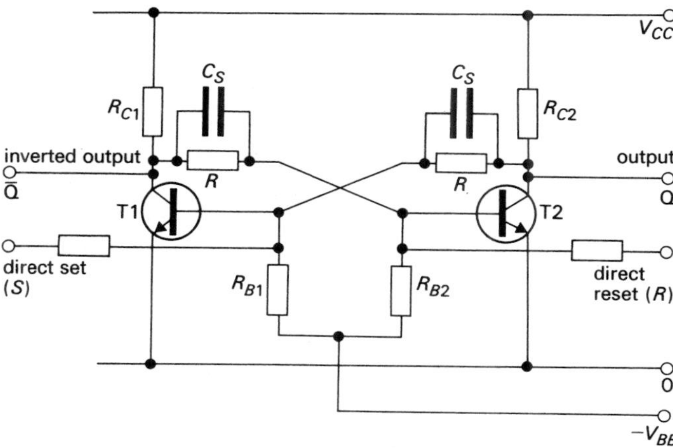

Figure 136 Bistable used as a one bit memory

condition with the RS bistable (as it is known). Other bistables, the circuits of which are beyond this level of Electronics, are used (notably the JK bistable).

It may be preferable to control the pulses reaching the bistable using a pulse steering network (see topic area Simple resistive capacitive networks) as shown in Figure 137.

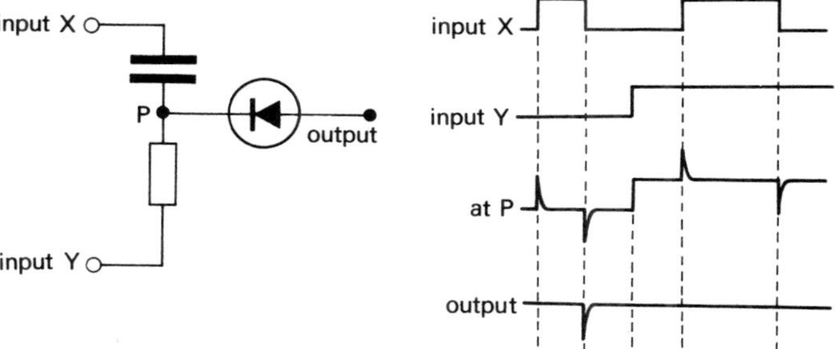

Figure 137 Single pulse network

The diode allows only negative-going pulses to be passed at the output, giving the correct biasing conditions. Positive signals are suppressed. When the voltage of Y is zero, the output level causes the negative pulses to bias the diode correctly, and these are passed through. If the voltage at Y is made greater than the magnitude of the negative pulses, the diode is never forward biased, and all the pulses are suppressed, i.e. the level of potential at Y is controlling the pulses at the output.

Consider two networks connected back to back as shown in Figure 138. Negative pulses at P are transmitted to the base of T2. Negative pulses at Q are transmitted to the base of T1.

Inputs Y and Z can be changed to positive levels at the correct time to stop the negative pulses passing through to either T1 or T2. Thus the pulses enter at input X, and the level of voltage at input Y or input Z steers the negative pulses in the described direction. It should be noted that the negative pulse is produced on the trailing edge of the input pulse appearing at input X. Overriding can still be carried out using the set and reset controls as shown in the circuit diagram of Figure 138.

Consider now the complete circuit diagram of a bistable device that has a pulse steering network and speed up capacitors, shown in Figure 139. When a positive input is applied, the capacitor C_{in} forms a differentiating circuit with the input resistance of the transistors. A peaky pulse waveform results, as shown in Figure 140.

This is ideal for fast switching. The diodes are reverse biased for negative pulses, and steer the positive pulse to the base of the *off* transistor (say T2). If T1 is *on* then the diode D1 is reverse biased via resistor R_1. As T2 is *off*, then diode D2 is forward biased by R_2, and consequently the first positive pulse passes through D2 and switches on T2. The collector voltage of T2 falls to zero volts, cutting off T1 and changing the biasing conditions of the diodes.

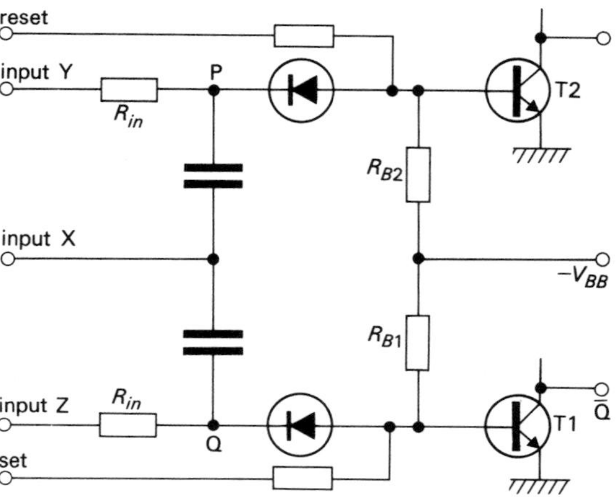

Figure 138 Pulse steering network

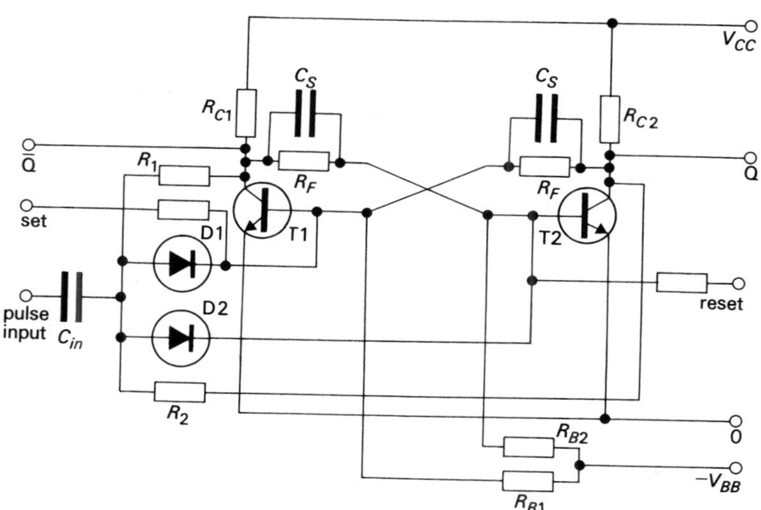

Figure 139 Bistable with steering network

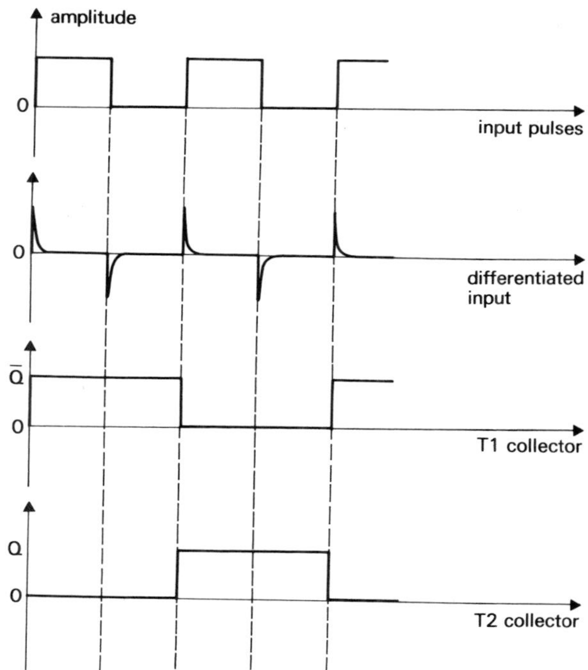

Figure 140 Pulse representation of the bistable and steering network

The following points should be noted:

(i) Each time an input pulse is applied, the circuit changes state.
(ii) The waveforms shown assume perfect switching characteristics. This is not true in practice; the voltage levels are slightly different from those shown.
(iii) Positive pulses applied at the inputs *R* and *S* set or reset the output as required.
(iv) The frequency of the output has now become half the input frequency – an ideal device for binary counting.
(v) The diodes can be arranged for triggering to occur using negative input pulses.
(vi) The bistable device can be used as a bistable multivibrator suitable for counting in binary code from a single pulse source. It is used with the other bistables required to complete the counter.

Self-assessment questions

Complete Questions 35–40 by writing in the correct word or deleting the incorrect word where applicable. The questions relate to astable, monostable and bistable oscillators.

35 The requirements of a transistor multivibrator are to produce in practice rectangular/sinusoidal waveforms that have the minimum/maximum distortion possible required for the particular desired circuit function.

36 The positive feedback in a multivibrator has a very tight/loose coupling to obtain the required waveform.

37 The p.d.f. of an astable multivibrator producing a square wave output is ____________.

38 The main feedback components of the astable multivibrator are resistive/capacitive elements only.

39 The main feedback components of the bistable multivibrator are resistive/capacitive elements only.

40 The monostable multivibrator has one/two stable state(s) only.

41 For the circuit diagrams shown in Figure 141, sketch the waveforms obtained at

(*a*) the base of T1 and the base of T2 for Figure 141(*a*) and (*b*) only
(*b*) the collector of T1 and the collector of T2 for Figure 141 (*a*), (*b*) and (*c*).

Assume steady state conditions apply for the astable and that the transistors operate as perfect switching devices.

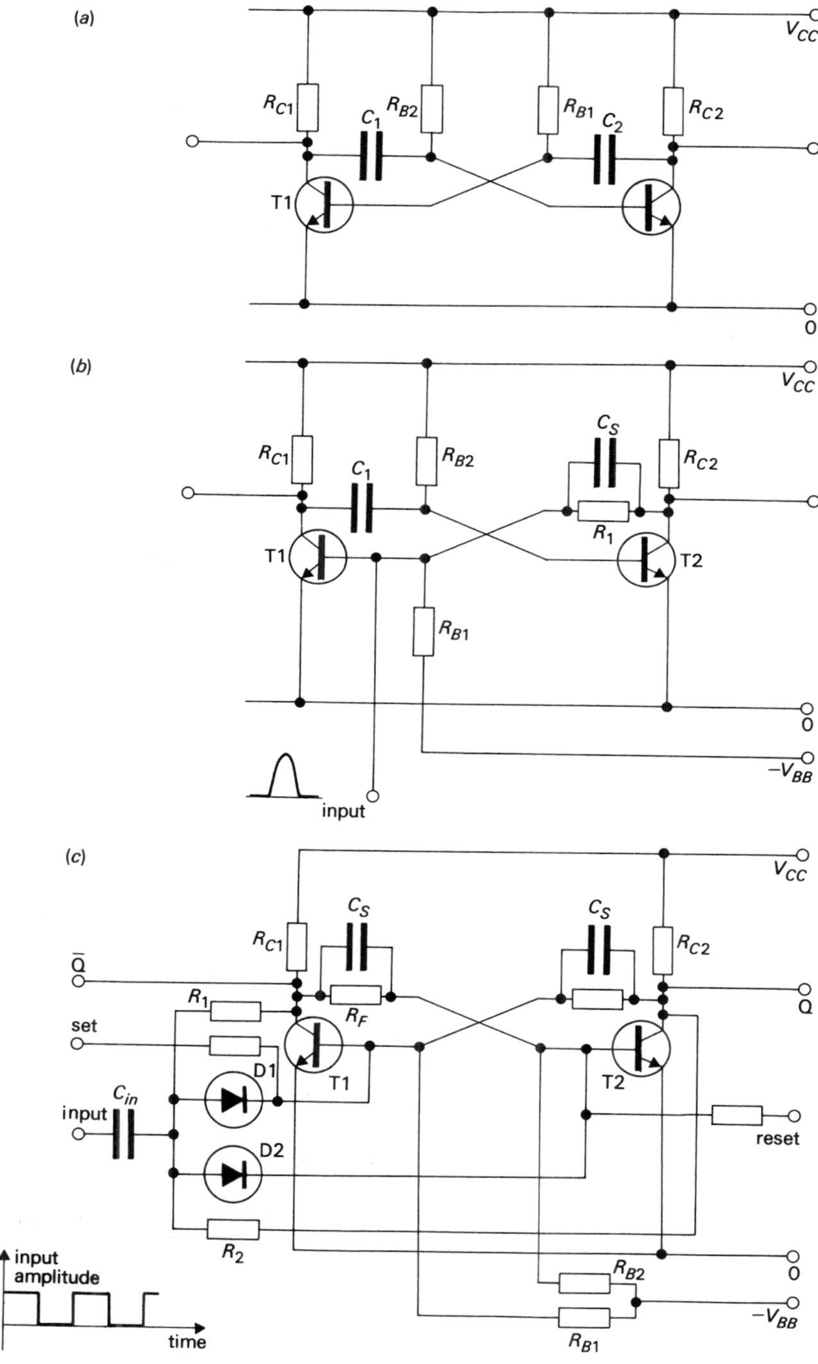

Figure 141 Circuit diagram for Self-assessment question 41

42 State one method for attaining accurate frequency control for an astable multivibrator.

43 State the main reason for diode triggering as used in the monostable device.

44 State the name of the circuit that converts the bistable circuit to a device suitable for binary counting.

The following questions relate to Figure 142.

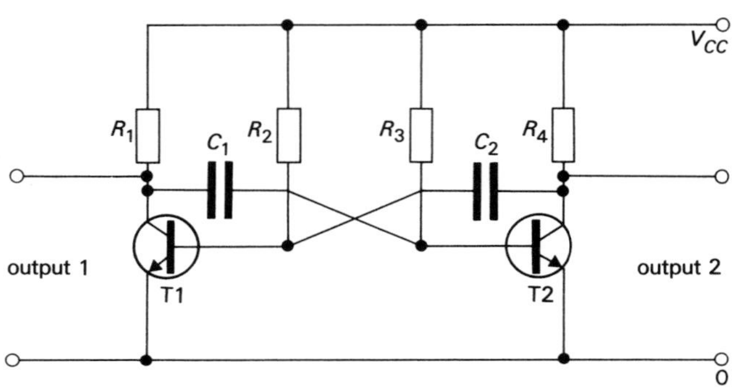

Figure 142 Circuit diagram for Self-assessment questions 45–52

45 The purpose of the circuit shown is to produce
(*a*) a sinewave output
(*b*) a circuit that has two stable states
(*c*) a single pulse of rectangular waveshape
(*d*) a train of rectangular pulses.

46 The input waveform
(*a*) is measured at output 1
(*b*) is measured at output 2
(*c*) is measured as a d.c. level
(*d*) is not measurable as there is no input waveform to the circuit.

47 If $R_2 = R_3$ and $C_1 = C_2$, the output waveform has a p.d.f. of
(*a*) 1
(*b*) 0·5
(*c*) 0·25
(*d*) greater than unity.

48 The purpose of the resistor R_1 is to
(*a*) provide the main current path for the current of T2

(*b*) provide a voltage drop which ensures that the collector potential of T1 is always held constant
(*c*) provide temperature stabilization for T1
(*d*) limit the collector current of T1

49 The purpose of the capacitor C_2 is to
(*a*) allow the base potential of T1 when the transistor is *off* to rise and switch T1 *on*
(*b*) allow the base potential of T1 when the transistor is *on* to rise and switch T1 *off*
(*c*) remove the ripple on the waveform measured at output 2
(*d*) remove the ripple on the waveform measured at the base of T2.

50 The purpose of the transistor T1 is to
(*a*) act as a switch that remains on for the whole of the periodic time of the repetition frequency
(*b*) act as a switch that remains off for the whole of the periodic time of the repetition frequency
(*c*) provide the energy source for the output waveform when the circuit is switched on
(*d*) provide a control for the energy distribution.

51 When the transistor T2 is switched on, the output at
(*a*) output 1 is approximately zero volts
(*b*) output 1 is approximately V_{CC} volts
(*c*) output 2 is approximately 0·5 V_{CC} volts
(*d*) output 2 is approximately V_{CC} volts.

52 The nearest approximate formula to determine the duration for which either transistor is switched on when $R_2 = R_3$ and $C_1 = C_2$ is
(*a*) $\tau_p = 0{\cdot}5\ C_2R_2$
(*b*) $\tau_p = 0{\cdot}6\ C_2R_2$
(*c*) $\tau_p = 0{\cdot}7\ C_2R_2$
(*d*) $\tau_p = 0{\cdot}8\ C_2R_2$

53 The repetition frequency of an astable multivibrator which is designed to give a square wave output is
(*a*) $f = \dfrac{1}{2\pi CR}$
(*b*) $f = \dfrac{1}{CR}$
(*c*) $f = \dfrac{1}{0{\cdot}7\tau_p}$
(*d*) $f = \dfrac{1}{2\tau_p}$

54 The astable multivibrator is a device that converts
(*a*) a d.c. waveform to an a.c. waveform
(*b*) a d.c. waveform to a unidirectional pulsating waveform
(*c*) a constant level waveform to a single pulsed output
(*d*) any input waveform to a rectangular output waveform.

Solutions to self-assessment questions (pages 149–151)

35 The requirements of a transistor multivibrator are to produce in practice rectangular waveforms that have the minimum distortion possible required for the particular desired circuit function.

36 The positive feedback in a multivibrator has a very tight coupling to obtain the required waveform.

37 0·5.

38 The main feedback components of the astable multivibrator are capacitive elements only.

39 The main feedback components of the bistable multivibrator are resistive elements only.

40 The monostable multivibrator has one stable state only.

41 These solutions are shown by
(*a*) Figure 129
(*b*) Figure 133
(*c*) Figure 140.

42 Synchronizing pulses are applied at the base of one of the transistors.

43 The main reason is prevention of the interaction of the triggering source and the oscillator upsetting the monostable operation.

44 Pulse steering network.

45 (*d*).

46 (*c*) The input energy is provided by V_{CC}.

47 (*b*).

48 (*d*).

49 (*a*).

50 (*d*).

51 (*b*).

52 (*b*).

53 (*c*).

54 (*b*).

Topic area Integrated circuits

After reading the following material, the reader shall:

10 Know the properties and applications of a range of linear integrated circuits (ICs).

10.1 Identify the manufacturing process of

(*a*) film ICs

(*b*) monolithic ICs.

10.2 State the advantages of ICs over discrete circuits.

10.3 Identify typical circuit symbols, manufacturers' representation of ICs and applications of ICs.

10.4 State the available range of linear ICs and their compatibility.

10.5 Give examples of performance characteristics of currently available linear integrated circuits in relation to

(*a*) Operational amplifiers

(*b*) Differential amplifiers

(*c*) Audio amplifiers

(*d*) R.f/i.f. amplifiers

(*e*) Wideband amplifiers.

One of the more recent revolutions in the electronics industry has been the integrated circuit (IC). To understand how so many of the previously described active devices (transistors, diodes, FETs, etc.) can be fitted into such a small space, and thus make possible the reduction of a computer from room size to desk size, it is necessary to look briefly at methods of construction of ICs.

Integrated circuits are made up from a small 'chip' or 'slice' of silicon onto which are diffused a large number of active devices (bipolar transistors, field effect devices and diodes) and passive devices (resistors and capacitors), suitably interconnected to form a complex circuit for a particular application. There are two main types of integrated circuit, one known as film ICs, the other as monolithic ICs.

The *film integrated circuit* may be sub-divided into two groups known as thick film and thin film devices. The interconnections, resistors and capacitors are deposited by printing the required 'patterns' of conductive or insulative materials on an insulated substrate (the physical support medium) such as glass or ceramic, the active devices being added after formation. This technique is analogous to a very miniaturized version of a printed circuit.

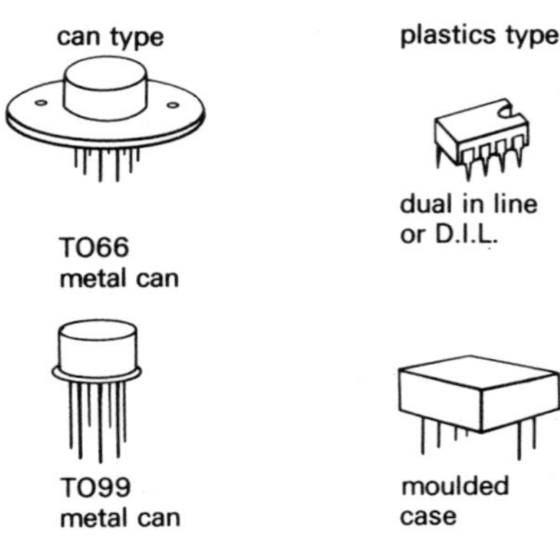

Figure 143 Example of encapsulated I Cs

In the *monolithic integrated circuits* active and passive devices are formed in one process. A p-type substrate is treated in such a way that an insulating oxide coating is applied. The layer is then covered by a photo-sensitive emulsion known as a photoresist, and exposed to ultra violet light through a pre-designed photographic mask. The light hardens the emulsion at 'low loss' portions of the mask but not at other parts where the mask is dense. The non-hardened emulsion is washed away exposing the oxide layer, which is then etched away. Impurities such as phosphorus are added to form n-type 'doped' silicon.

The process is repeated as many times as necessary to produce the various junctions required to form all the active and passive circuit elements of the device. Resistors are formed by the basic semiconductor material, its resistivity being controlled by the magnitude of the doping level. Capacitors may be simulated either by reverse biased diodes, or alternatively using the oxide coating as a dielectric between metallic tabs. Inductors are difficult to produce and are therefore usually designed out of the circuit, but if unavoidable, discrete components are added externally. Gold wires are used for all external connections and the device is encapsulated either in plastics or in a metal can, as shown in Figure 143.

The manufacture of system blocks dates from about 1959, and stems from the basic idea that it is wasteful and unnecessary to make all the separate components (in particular transistors, diodes and capacitors) individually, mount them in protective packages one by one, and then interconnect them to form the circuit block (see Figure 144 for a typical example).

The manufacture of integrated circuits:

(*a*) Avoids the individual packaging of parts which is wasteful of materials, labour and space

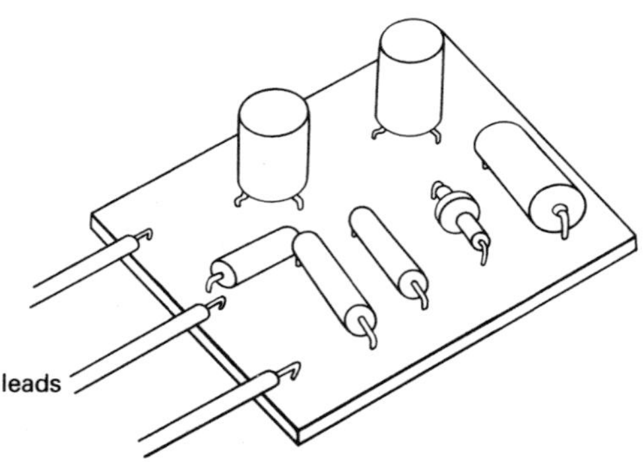

Figure 144 Discrete component technology

(*b*) Avoids the discrepancies (varying tolerances) of discrete components made at different times and different places

(*c*) Reduces the number of connection joints compared to an equivalent discrete technology block (see topic area Noise)

(*d*) Reduces the number of long leads that are used in discrete technology, and thus reduces the effects of change in impedance of these connections at high frequencies

(*e*) Results in circuits that are superior in regard to cost, technical specification, reliability and size (miniaturization) compared with equivalent discrete component circuits.

The tooling cost is high for each individual IC and they cannot be made economically in batches of less than a few hundreds. The real cost advantages are not apparent until production numbers are high. Thus a circuit designer cannot specify his circuit needs (except in special computing cases); instead he must accept an existing mass produced IC and modify it using external discrete components where necessary.

At the present time of writing there is a large range of available ICs for a wide variety of applications. This means that an IC can have anything from a small number to a large number of different pin connections, the number of which depends on the particular application for which the IC is used. Figure 145 illustrates typical examples.

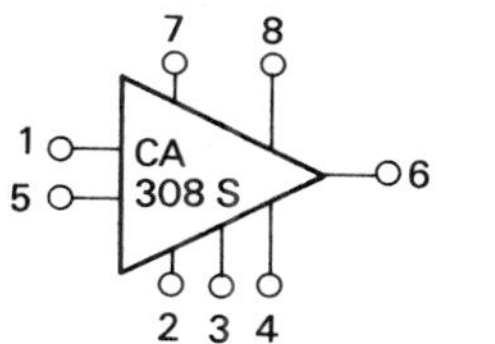

precision operational amplifier

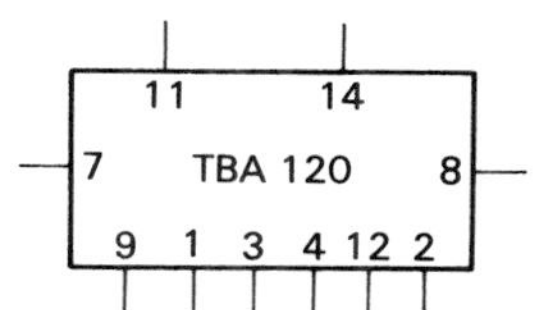

i.f. amplifier for f.m. radio

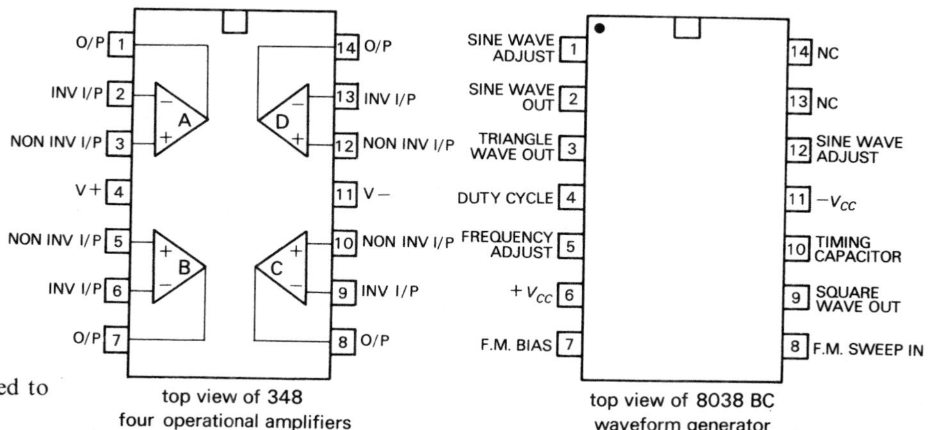

top view of 348
four operational amplifiers

top view of 8038 BC
waveform generator

Figure 145 Symbols used to represent I Cs

The rectangle and the triangle are normally used in circuit diagrams. Manufacturers either mark in the circuit functions where possible, or label the positions as shown in the diagram. The symbols shown represent operational amplifiers, a waveform generator and an i.f. amplifier for f.m. radio. However, many other types of ICs exist; they can be broadly divided into two groups.

(*a*) Digital: these are based on discrete changes occurring in the circuit function. They contain logic gates, monostables, bistables, astables, adders, counters, registers, timers, and many more.

(*b*) Analogue (linear): these are based on circuits that operate under linear conditions of change. They contain a wide range of different types of amplifiers, filters, oscillators, waveform generators, to name but a few.

In the topic area Amplifiers, an introduction to the differential amplifier was given. A simple circuit of the amplifier is shown in Figure 146.

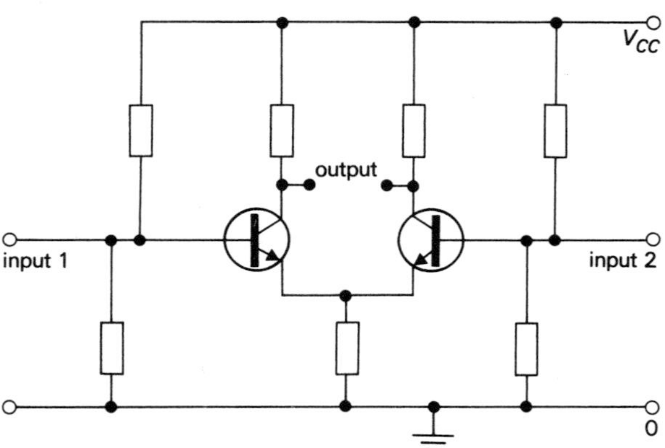

Figure 146 A simple differential amplifier

The differential amplifier is most effective when employed in very low frequency amplification where signals and drift are often difficult to separate. The effectiveness of drift rejection is one of the main reasons why differential amplifiers form the basis of many IC configurations. When used in integrated circuits, differential amplifiers are interconnected to form linear amplifiers operating from d.c. to v.h.f. They can be employed in circuits such as r.f./i.f. amplifiers, limiters, demodulators, mixers and operational amplifiers. A simple circuit of an operational amplifier is shown in Figure 147. The figure shows two simple differential amplifiers directly coupled in cascade feeding into an emitter follower stage, from which the output is taken.

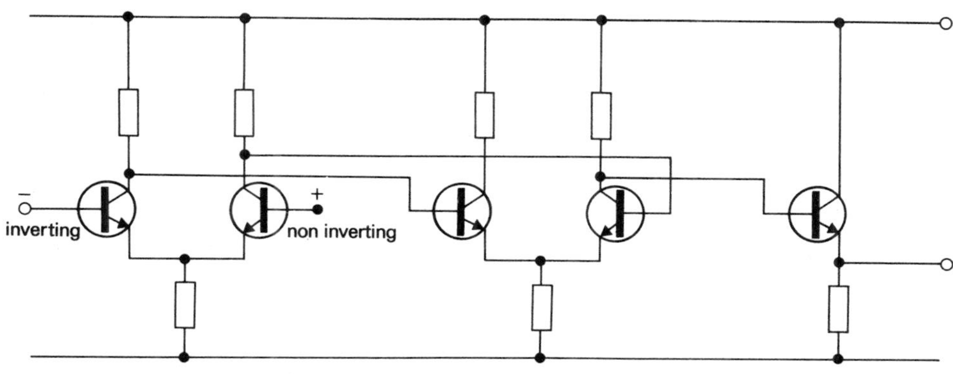

Figure 147 Basic circuit of an operational amplifier

virtual earth point

R_F

R

P

R_D

v_{in}

v_{out}

$$\text{gain} = \frac{v_{out}}{v_{in}} = \frac{R_F}{R}$$

igure 148 A simple operational verting amplifier

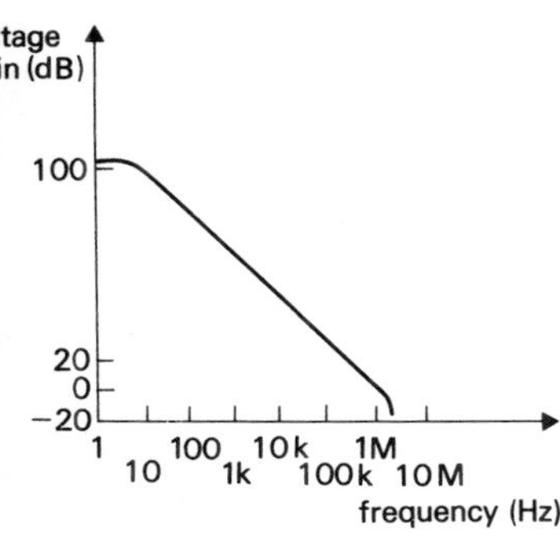

gure 149 Typical manufacturer's ecification

(*a*) *Operational amplifiers*

Operational amplifiers are basically very high gain, direct coupled amplifiers which rely on feedback to control their stability and response characteristic. They contain cascaded differential amplifiers of the type indicated in Figure 146 which provide high immunity to drift. They are often employed as video amplifiers, frequency shaping amplifiers, integrators, differentiators or comparator amplifiers, the latter often being used to perform mathematical operations in analogue computers.

Gain values in the region of 100 dB and input impedances in excess of 1–2 MΩ are obtained from operational amplifiers. A typical circuit is shown in Figure 148. With typical gain figures in excess of 100 000 times, an output voltage of 10 volts results from an input voltage of $10/100\,000 = 100\ \mu\text{V}$. This is so small that the point P on Figure 148 is virtually at earth potential and is known as a virtual earth. Negative feedback applied from the output to input controls the very high gain, reducing it to the required value by the amount of feedback applied. The amount of feedback is set by the values chosen for R and R_F.

A typical operational amplifier available at the present time is the 741. The manufacturer's characteristics are shown in Figure 149 which illustrates the gain/frequency response.

The ideal characteristics for the operational amplifier are

voltage gain	: infinitely large
drift	: zero
bandwidth	: infinitely large
input impedance	: infinitely large
output impedance	: zero

Although these are extreme specifications, commercially available units approach the ideal so closely that many practical circuits can be designed on the basis of the above characteristics. In practice, the ICs generally require the addition of discrete components (mostly resistors and/or capacitors) to set the gain or to determine the purpose of the device.

(*b*) *Differential amplifiers*

It has been established that differential amplifiers are most effective when used in low frequency applications for their high drift rejection properties. They have a differential (double ended) input and a single-ended output. They are available as low cost, general purpose amplifiers used for comparison of one signal with another. The comparison may be between two d.c. signals, (e.g. voltage stabilizer to compare the output voltage with a reference voltage), or between a.c. signals. The main advantage of differential amplifiers is that they can work from small supply voltages of the order $\pm 2{\cdot}5$ V, which make them compatible with computer circuits.

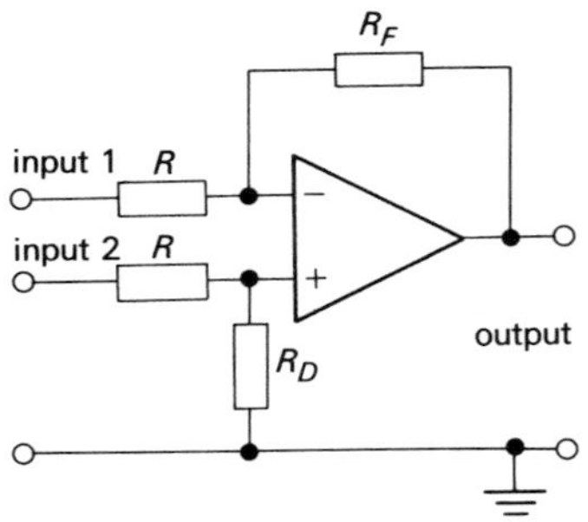

It should be noted that the operational amplifier can also be used as a differential amplifier, the increased cost being balanced by the improvement in characteristics. A typical circuit is as shown in Figure 150.

Figure 150 Differential amplifier using an operational amplifier

(*c*) *Audio amplifiers*

Audio amplifiers can be divided into two classes, small signal amplifiers and power amplifiers. Small signal amplifiers are required to produce a constant gain over a specified bandwidth which at most is of the order 30 Hz–30 kHz. Power amplifiers are used at audio frequencies to give maximum power in for example a loudspeaker. The characteristics of both classes have been described in topic area Amplifiers.

When used in ICs there is a wide variety of choice of devices for use as audio amplifiers. Small signal amplifiers generally require the addition of discrete components, mostly capacitors, to adjust the gain/frequency response and for coupling/decoupling purposes.

Power amplifiers generally use driver stages as ICs together with output transistors mounted on heat sinks to improve output power dissipation for both class A and class B operation. They can however be used as a complete IC for power ratings of up to about 5 W. A typical example of this is the MFC 6070 which is designed primarily for low cost amplifiers in record players, televisions and radio applications. Typical manufacturers' data include

100 mV sensitivity for 1 W
Low distortion: 1 per cent at 1 W typical
Short circuit proof – short term (10 seconds typical)

No heat sink required for 1 W output at $T_A = 55°C$
(T_A is the ambient temperature)
Excellent hum rejection.

(d) *R.f./i.f. amplifiers*

The primary function of r.f. amplifiers is to improve the signal/noise ratio of a receiver, and to reject the spurious response of the second channel (known as image rejection). This improves the pre-mixer selectivity due to the added tuned circuit (see Figure 151).

It is not usual to fit r.f. stages in 'normal' m.w./l.w. receivers because the existing signal/noise ratio is adequate. However they may be fitted in receivers where noise is high, e.g. car radio receivers, communications receivers, and receivers operating in the v.h.f./u.h.f. spectrum.

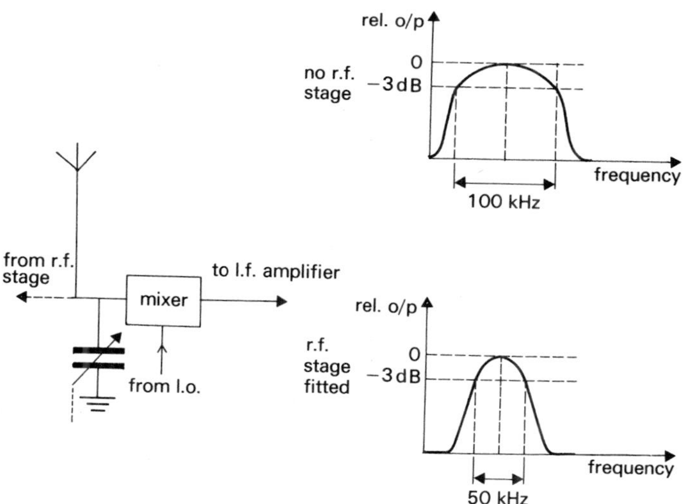

Figure 151 Effect of adding an r.f. stage

The purposes of i.f. amplifiers are to provide most of the receiver amplification (about 80 per cent) over an accurately defined bandwidth, and to provide all the selectivity of the receiver. The operational passband is therefore determined by an i.f. amplifier.

Both r.f. and i.f. amplifiers are in many respects similar to amplifiers operating in the audio/video spectrum, except that r.f. and i.f. amplifiers use inductive or tuned circuit loads as an alternative to resistive loads. Thus the signals are amplified over narrow bandwidths, and reject much of the accompanying noise present in r.f. signals. When integrated circuits are used for r.f./i.f. amplifiers, they are used with the addition of discrete components (mostly tuning inductance and sometimes capacitance) to set the frequency of the tuned circuit. A typical example is the MC 1550 r.f./i.f. amplifier which is used for communications applications.

Consider the basic diagram of an f.m. receiver using three ICs as shown in Figure 152. A1 acts as a low noise amplifier at 90 MHz. The local oscillator (l.o.) operates at 100·7 MHz which with a mixer results in an output signal at 10·7 MHz. The 10·7 MHz filter (usually a crystal or a ceramic resonator) shapes the response characteristic before i.f. amplification. This method is used because of the problem of including inductors within the IC. A2 amplifies the 10·7 MHz signal by about 80 dB, demodulates the i.f. and provides an autiomatic gain control system. A3 amplifies the audio output from A2 by about 12 dB to produce a power output of about 4 W at the loudspeaker.

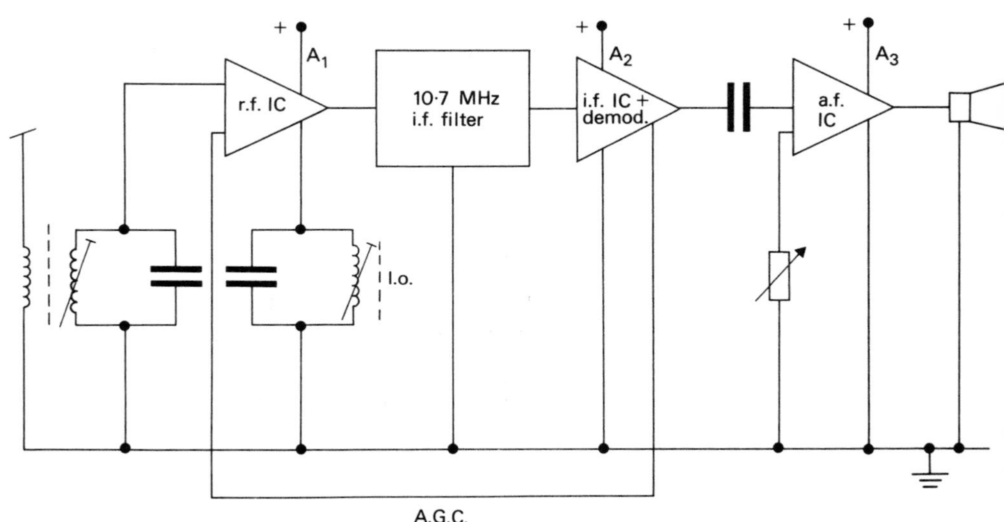

Figure 152 Diagram of f.m. receiver using three ICs

(*e*) *Wideband amplifiers*

Wideband amplifiers have a flat gain/frequency response over a very wide frequency range. They may require discrete components together with the IC to set the bandwidth. They are used mainly as video amplifiers for t.v. circuits where stable voltage gain, low distortion and wide bandwidth are required. A typical example of this is the MC 1552 G which is an IC intended for use as either a wideband linear amplifier or a fast rise pulse amplifier.

As there is such a wide range of manufacturers' information available it is impossible to reproduce it in detail in this book. However, it is suggested that the reader now enlarges on the details given here by investigating further manufacturers' data of the ICs that have been mentioned, namely:

741, CA 308 S, TBA 120, 348, 8038 BC,
MFC 6070, MC 1550, and MC 1552 G

Self-assessment questions

Fill in the missing word or words where applicable for the Questions 1 to 6.

1 When ICs are formed by depositing required patterns for resistors, capacitors and interconnections on an insulated substrate, they are called __________ integrated circuits.

2 When ICs are formed such that active and passive devices are formed in one process, they are called __________ integrated circuits.

3 ICs which are based on discrete circuit changes are called__________ ICs.

4 ICs which are based on linear circuit changes are called __________ ICs.

5 In general, ICs are not used singly to provide a complete circuit function, but are used together with __________ __________.

6 The change in voltage levels due to supply variations or temperature changes when using the circuit shown in Figure 153 is called __________.

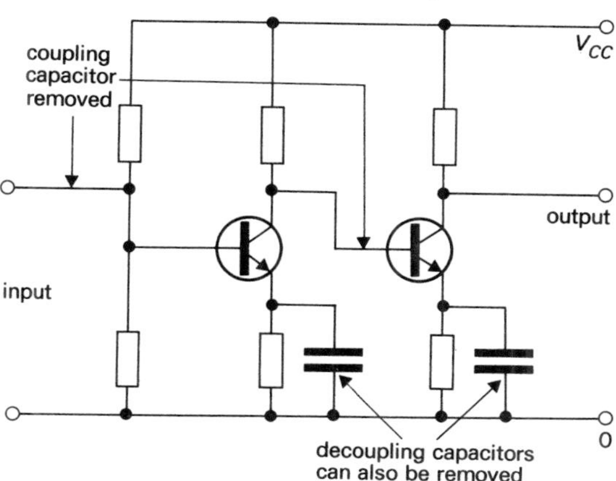

Figure 153 Diagram for self-assessment question 6

7 List four advantages of IC technology when compared with discrete component technology.

8 State one disadvantage of the IC technology compared to discrete component technology.

9 For the diagram shown in Figure 154 tick the correct statement
(*a*) Both are circuit symbols
(*b*) Both are manufacturer's representations
(*c*) Diagram (i) is a circuit symbol
(ii) is a manufacturer's representation
(*d*) Diagram (i) is a manufacturer's representation
(ii) is a circuit symbol.

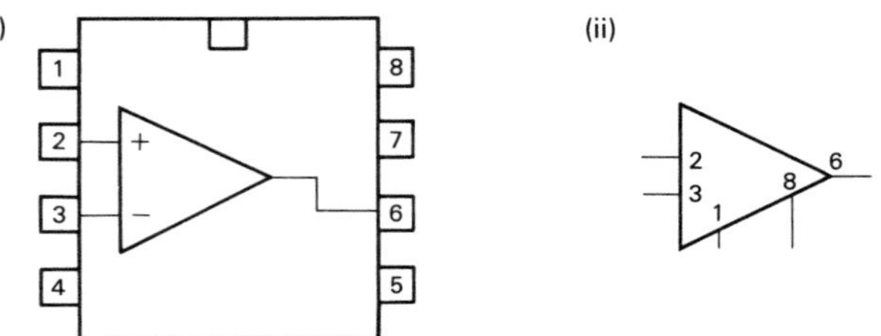

Figure 154 Diagram for Self-assessment question 9

Select the correct alternative and/or fill in the missing word(s) for Questions 10–18.

10 A differential amplifier is generally a low/high cost amplifier and is mainly used for amplification/comparison of input signals.

11 Small signal audio amplifiers are required to produce a constant/infinite gain over a specified bandwidth.

12 Power audio amplifiers are used to maximize/minimize power at a.f./r.f. frequencies.

13 The primary function of an r.f. amplifier when used in receivers is to improve the __________ __________.

14 The primary function of an i.f. amplifier when used in receivers is to improve the __________ __________.

15 Wideband amplifiers have a gain-frequency response from a few hertz to __________.

16 The main purpose of the operational amplifier is to provide a very high/low voltage gain, direct coupled amplifier which relies on ____________ to control its stability and response.

17 The main 'building block' circuit used to construct operational amplifiers in ICs is called a ____________ amplifier.

18 The main purpose of an operational amplifier is to provide a very high/low voltage gain, direct coupled amplifier.

19 Match the following properties (labelled A, B, etc.) of the perfect operational amplifier to their values labelled 1 and 2, by placing the numbers next to each letter.

A voltage gain	1 infinitely large
B drift	2 zero
C bandwidth	
D input impedance	
E output impedance	

20 The bandwidth of a high quality small signal audio amplifier is:

A 3–30 Hz
B 3–3000 Hz
C 30–3000 Hz
D 30–30 000 Hz
E 0–300 000 Hz

Tick the correct alternative.

21 List four circuit applications for
(*a*) linear ICs
(*b*) digital ICs.

Topic area Stabilized power supplies

After reading the following material, the reader shall:

11 Know the basic circuit techniques utilized in stabilized power supplies.

11.1 Identify the requirements for maintaining a constant voltage output across the load.

11.2 Sketch a block diagram of a series stabilized power supply using the comparator technique.

11.3 Explain the operation of the power supply given in **11.2.**

11.4 Draw a typical circuit diagram of a complete regulated power supply which uses the comparator technique.

Most electronic equipment such as amplifiers, transmitters, receivers and computers, contain active devices such as transistors which require a d.c. supply for their operation. The d.c. supply may be obtained from three sources: batteries, d.c. generators, or it may be derived from an a.c. source. From previous considerations it may be recalled that a.c. can be converted into d.c. by means of rectifying and smoothing circuits. The most common power supplies used in electronic equipment such as signal generators, oscilloscopes, hi-fi amplifiers, bench power supply units or televisions, utilize the standard 240 V, 50 Hz a.c. mains supply. In such power supplies the output voltage may vary for several reasons.

If *no load* current is taken, the output voltage may not be a steady d.c. value because of

(*a*) variation in the energy of the supply source. This is usually caused by fluctuations in the a.c. mains supply

(*b*) external factors such as changes in ambient temperature or ageing of components.

If *load* current is taken, the output voltage may not be a steady d.c. value because of

(i) the voltage drop across the internal impedance of the supply. This is generally caused by transformers and rectifiers;

(ii) the average voltage drop across the reservoir capacitor due to the rate of discharge required to supply the load current.

It is due to all these factors that the practical output voltage of a power supply unit may deteriorate as the load current increases. This is illustrated by the curve of Figure 155 for an unstabilized power supply. The curve is often referred to as the *regulation curve* of the power supply. The regulation curve can be improved by simple circuits employing either a cold cathode gas-filled diode or a solid state zener diode. These circuits are employed in power supplies where regulation is of little consequence, for example in small amplifier circuits (less than 2 V) or battery chargers.

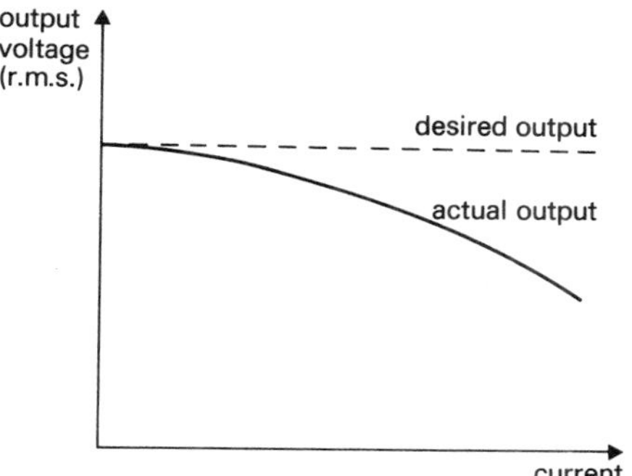

Figure 155 Regulation curve of an unstabilized d.c. power supply

Whenever a constant p.d. is required at the output terminals, more complex circuits are used such as a negative feedback network containing a differential amplifier (comparator). These may be found in stabilized bench power supplies, hi-fi amplifiers, television sound reproduction systems and relays in telephone exchanges.

The power supply which is required for any application can only be determined from details of the particular application with which the power supply is utilized.

Figure 156 illustrates a block diagram of a typical regulated power supply as may be found in some sine/square wave oscillators, logic circuit power supplies, oscilloscopes, laboratory power supplies, telephone exchanges or televisions. The unstabilized or unregulated output from the d.c. power supply is fed to the control device, which improves the regulation. The feedback network, which is usually a potential divider, feeds a proportion of the output voltage to the comparison device/circuit. Here, a proportion of the output voltage and the voltage from the reference device (usually a zener diode) is compared. It is the difference between the two voltages which is then applied to the control device. The output level is brought to the required level by the control device, and the regulation of the output is improved. Sometimes overload protection is included in the regulated power supply unit to limit the output current to a predetermined value; this is useful in bench power supplies.

Solutions to self-assessment questions (pages 161–163)

1 Film.

2 Monolithic.

3 Digital.

4 Linear or analogue.

5 Discrete components.

6 Drift.

7 The advantages of IC technology when compared with discrete component technology include:
Individual packaging of parts is avoided
Variations in component tolerances do not occur
The number of connection joints is reduced
The number of long leads is reduced
ICs are superior in regard to reliability and technical specification, and mass produced
ICs are cheaper compared with equivalent discrete devices.

8 High tooling cost for the 'one off' IC.

9 (*d*).

10 Low comparison.

11 Constant,

12 Maximize a.f.

13 Signal-to-noise or signal-to-noise ratio.

14 Receiver amplification (and determine the passband).

15 Megahertz.

16 High feedback.

17 Differential.

18 High.

19 A1 B2 C1 D1 E2.

20 D.

21
a) Wide range of amplifiers, oscillators, signal generators, modulators, mixers, filters
b) Logic gates, monostables, bistables, astables, timers, registers.

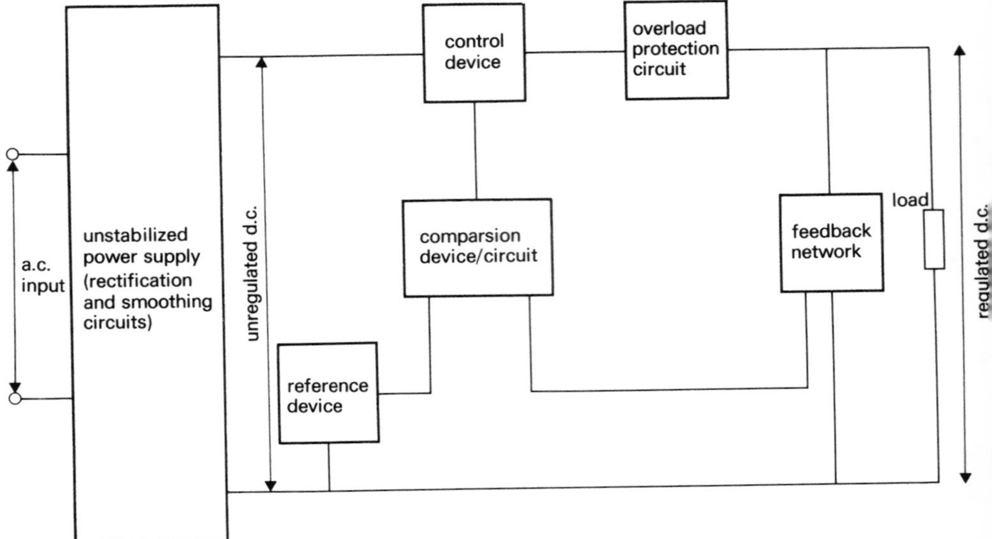

Figure 156 Block diagram of a regulated power supply

Typical subcircuits of a regulated power supply

Typical sub-circuits include:

(*i*) *Control device*

Control devices are usually active devices, e.g. transistors. They may be classified into two categories:

(*a*) *series regulators* which are connected in series with the load, and
(*b*) *shunt regulators* which are connected in parallel with the load.

Figure 157(*a*) shows a series transistor regulator, which is simply an emitter follower. The voltage reference source is a zener diode which maintains the base of the transistor at constant potential. Any change in the load resistance causes the load voltage to change. This causes the base–emitter voltage of the transistor to alter accordingly, which in turn alters the base current and hence the collector current. Thus the output voltage is restored to the required level. In this type of regulator, the transistor must pass the full load current, I_L, at all times.

Figure 157(*b*) shows a shunt transistor regulator which is connected in parallel with the load. A decrease in the load resistance causes the load current I_L to increase, and the load voltage to increase. The collector current of the shunt transistor thus decreases, and since the base–collector voltage is held constant by the reference device (zener diode), the base–emitter voltage causes the base current to decrease. Hence the load voltage is restored to the required level.

The zener diode is the reference source of both circuits. Inherent feedback is used but without the comparator device. With both circuits, as the mains voltage increases, the output voltage increases. This has the effect of changing the circuit conditions such that the required voltage output level is restored and stabilization is improved.

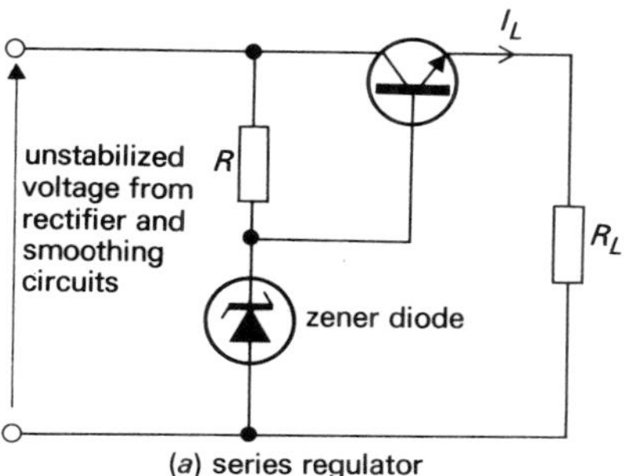

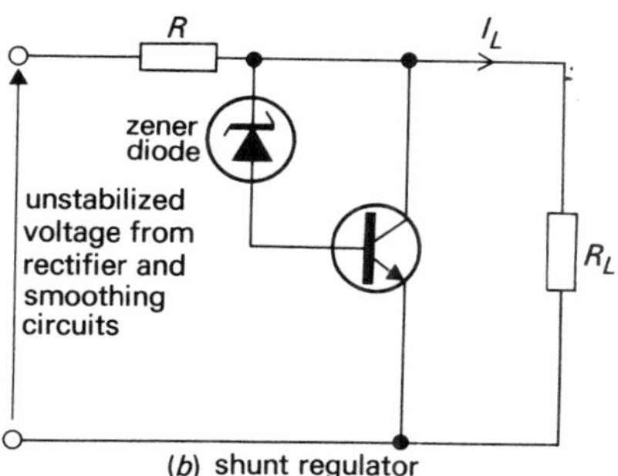

Figure 157 Transistor regulators

(*ii*) *Comparison circuit*, with a feedback network and reference device.

Figure 158 shows a typical comparison circuit incorporating a feedback network and reference device. The comparison circuit is a differential amplifier consisting of a transistor T1 and resistor *R*. The feedback network is the potential divider resistors R_1 and R_2. The reference device is the zener diode Z_{D1}. Suppose a fraction (β) of the output voltage (V_0) is fed back to the base of the transistor from the potential divider network. The input voltage to the base of the transistor is therefore ($\beta V_0 - V_Z$). The emitter of T1 is held at constant potential (V_Z) by the zener diode. When the output voltage increases the base voltage ($\beta V_0 - V_Z$) also increases which causes the collector potential to fall. This causes a reduction of the control device potential (the base of a transistor in a series regulator), which restores the output current and voltage to the required level.

The operation of this circuit is simple and is easily constructed, but its disadvantages are

(*a*) It draws current from the feedback network
(*b*) It has a poor temperature coefficient
(*c*) It drives current through the reference device.

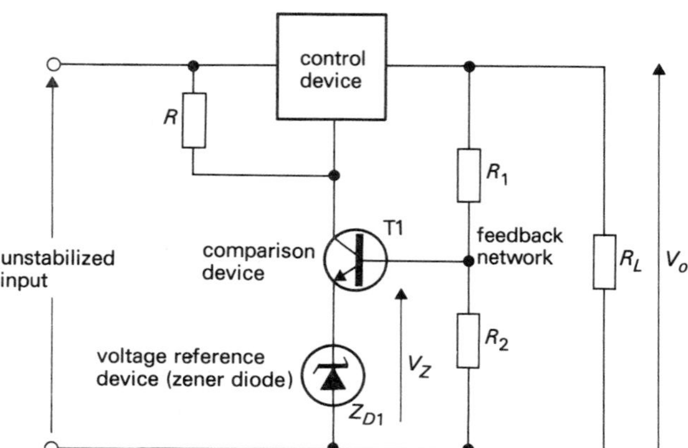

Figure 158 Comparison circuit, with feedback network and reference device

With the advent of integrated circuits, operational amplifiers are available which operate as differential amplifiers (see topic area Integrated circuits). A more sophisticated regulated power supply is shown in Figure 159. The comparison device is the 741 operational amplifier. Notice that the reference device is taken from the output, and the value of R_2 must be chosen to ensure that the zener diode has sufficient current flowing through it to bring it to its correct operating conditions.

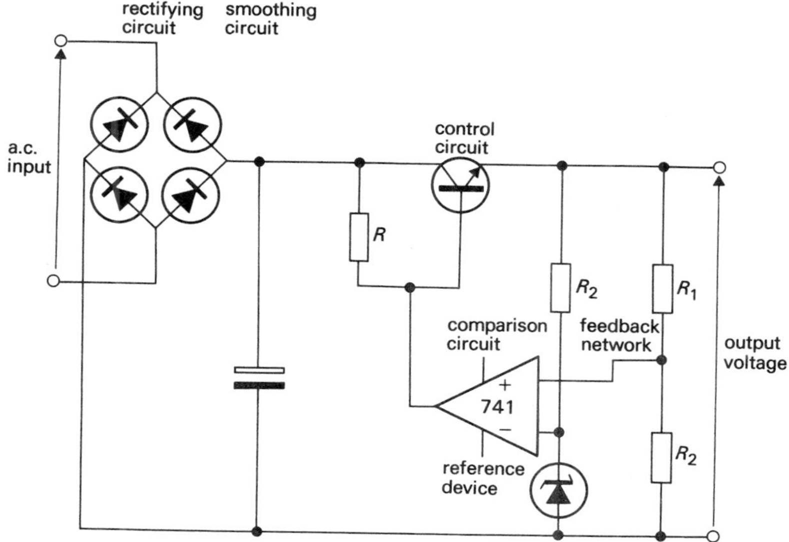

Figure 159 A complete regulated power supply incorporating an operational amplifier

Self-assessment questions

1 Statement 1: Circuits with poor regulation have varying output voltage and current when the load resistance changes.
Statement 2: An unregulated power supply contains a rectifier and smoothing circuit only.

(*a*) Only statement 1 is true
(*b*) Only statement 2 is true
(*c*) Both statements 1 and 2 are true
(*d*) Neither statement 1 nor 2 is true.

Underline the correct answer.

2 List the various sub-circuits utilized in a regulated power supply unit.

3 Statement 1: There are two types of control device

(i) series regulators, and
(ii) shunt regulators.

Statement 2: Both series and shunt regulators are connected across the load.

(*a*) Only statement 1 is true
(*b*) Only statement 2 is true
(*c*) Both statements 1 and 2 are true
(*d*) Neither statement 1 nor 2 is true.

Underline the correct answer.

4 Match the typical devices labelled (*a*) to (*g*) to the sub-circuits of a regulated power unit which are labelled 1 to 6, by placing the letters (*a*) to (*g*) next to the particular sub-circuit.

(1) Rectifying circuit	(a) Power diode
(2) Smoothing circuit	(b) Zener diode
(3) Control circuit	(c) Resistor
(4) Feedback network	(d) Power transistor
(5) Comparison device	(e) Reservoir capacitor
(6) Reference device	(f) Field effect transistor
	(g) Operational amplifier

Each letter may be used once, more than once or not at all.

5 Sketch a diagram of a regulated power supply which includes the following sub-circuits:

(1) Unregulated d.c. circuit
(2) Reference device
(3) Feedback network
(4) Overload protection circuit
(5) Control device
(6) Load resistor

6 List three factors which affect the output of a power supply unit.

Solutions to self-assessment questions (pages 169–170)

1 (*c*).

2 (1) Reference device
(2) Comparison circuit
(3) Control device
(4) Overload protection circuit
(5) Feedback network
(6) Unstabilized power supply.

3 (*a*) Series regulators are connected in series with the load. Shunt regulators are connected in parallel with the load.

4 (1) Rectifying circuit (*a*)
(2) Smoothing circuit (*e*)
(2) Control circuit (*d*)
(4) Feedback network (*c*)
(5) Comparison device (*g*) or (*d*) and (*c*)
(6) Reference device (*b*)

5 See Figure 156 or Figure 159.

6 (1) Variation in the a.c. mains supply.
(2) Changes in ambient temperature or ageing of components.
(3) Voltage drops across devices of the power supply such as transformers, rectifiers and capacitors, due to their rate of discharge.

Index

amplifiers, 37–64
  applications, 37
  audio frequency, 42
  biasing, 40–1
  buffer, 44
  complementary, 63
  differential, 50
  input impedance, 50, 55–6
  push-pull, 61–3
  radio frequency, 42–3
  single ended, 61
  tuned, 42–3
  wideband, 43–4
CR networks, 97–109
  applications, 109
  coupling circuit, 106
  decay time, 102
  differentiating circuit, 106–109
  five time constants, 102, 106
  integrating circuit, 106–109
  rise time, 102
  time constant, 102
distortion
  amplitude, 59
  frequency, 59
  harmonic, 59
  intermodulation, 60
  phase, 60
feedback, 75–93
  applications, 75, 87, 93
  bandwidth, 84
  gain expression, 78–81
  gain stability, 82–4
  input resistance, 86–7
  negative, 83–7
FETs, 9–35
  advantages, 9, 34
  applications, 9
  biasing, 10–13, 25–6
  common source, 24–5
  construction, 10–15
  depletion mode, 13–15
  enhancement mode, 15
  operation, 13–15
  output characteristics, 16–18
  precautions, 21
  transfer characteristics, 18–21
ICs, 153–61
  advantages, 153–5
  audio frequency, 158–9
  differential, 156, 158
  disadvantages, 155
  linear, 156
  manufacture, 153–4
  operational, 157–8
  performance, 156–61
  r.f./i.f., 159–60
  wideband, 160–1
interstage coupling
  direct, 48, 50–1
  frequency response, 54
  R–C, 51–4
noise, 68–73
  definition, 68–9
  external, 69–70
  internal, 70
  precautions, 69–70
  signal-to-noise ratio, 71–3
oscillators, 113–48
  astable, 135–40
  biasing, 122–3
  bistable, 143–8
  crystal, 130–1
  feedback, 116–20
  frequency, stability, 128–31
  ladder network, 123–6
  LC, 121–2
  monostable, 141–3
  negative resistance, 116
  RC, 123–8
  relaxation, 116
  synchronization, 139–40
  triggering, 141–3
  Wien network, 126–8
parasitic oscillations, 63–4
power supplies, series stabilized, 164–9
  comparison circuits, 167–8
  control device, 166–7
  regulation, 164–5
pulse duty factor, 137